The *Listening* Touch

To Debbie
Together in Touch
Lynn Dubois

The Listening Touch

A Hands-on Gift

Lynn Dubois

MOUNTAIN ARBOR PRESS

Mountain Arbor
Press
Alpharetta, GA

The author has tried to recreate events, locations, and conversations from her memories of them. In some instances, in order to maintain their anonymity, the author has changed the names of individuals and places. She may also have changed some identifying characteristics and details such as physical attributes, occupations, and places of residence.

ISBN: 978-1-6653-0419-1 - Paperback
eISBN: 978-1-6653-0420-7 - eBook

These ISBNs are the property of Mountain Arbor Press for the express purpose of sales and distribution of this title. The content of this book is the property of the copyright holder only. Mountain Arbor Press does not hold any ownership of the content of this book and is not liable in any way for the materials contained within. The views and opinions expressed in this book are the property of the Author/Copyright holder, and do not necessarily reflect those of Mountain Arbor Press.

Printed in the United States of America   0 4 0 5 2 2

♾ This paper meets the requirements of ANSI/NISO Z39.48-1992 (Permanence of Paper)

My husband, Ernie,
son and daughter-in-law, Lee and Diane,
and son, Elton,
Grandchildren: Tobias, Caden, and Aleke

CONTENTS

Preface

February 1992—At the age of forty-one, I was informed that my services would no longer be needed as my supervisor handed me a cardboard box to get my things collected to leave my job of eleven years.

A corporate merger and economic downturn also known as downsizing. I packed up my personal belongings to leave my office as I was being watched from around a corner. My desk was near the door because I was a receptionist, so I slipped out unnoticed, except for one, never to return.

I felt sorry for the person to sit in my position the next morning, for I knew each line of my thirty-five-line console switchboard, but the next person wouldn't. It would be only temporary for her anyway, but challenging no doubt. Very few people wanted my job of answering incoming calls from outside the company, as well as being a backup for all calls from within the company. I often envisioned myself as a combat soldier on the front lines, ready for battle with each call. It was my job to make everyone within the company sound, or "look," good over the phone. I walked across the parking lot, put my box in the back seat, and drove home.

The next morning, I woke up at my usual time, saw my husband off to work, and kids off to school, while I had nowhere to be except home. It's a strange feeling when that happens. I slipped back into bed to take in the shock and think about the person who would be at my desk.

My job was being eliminated, but the company would have someone sit in for the short time during the transition to a new phone system that would soon include voicemail. With my product knowledge and seniority, I didn't expect this. I thought I would be valuable elsewhere. I reached for the phone to call my former desk, and it was Gale—just so she would know the console. She was retiring in a few months, and I could tell she was crying as I identified myself. I told her I was sorry, but I was blindsided by the news and didn't have time to mark the phone, and she didn't know where she was going until that morning. She felt better after I told her which line was whose from memory.

I could hear a bit of a smile in her voice after that, and I didn't blame her for what happened. She, too, was sorry for what happened as we said good-bye.

I can't remember ever seeing her again!

Now I was free from Corporate America, or at least for now.

I had started working on a line on the night shift. Then I advanced to an office position and into the corporate office. Because of my knowledge of products and of people in the corporation, I got outside callers to the right person quickly. Besides answering phones, I did the office newsletters, as well as other duties within the corporate office. Many of the secretaries would even call me asking about products when they needed details. This was a time when you worked for a company, and after a number of loyal years, you could advance and then retire with a pension, social security, and a bit of investment savings, and you'd be set for a happily-ever-after retirement. That was my long-term plan.

Plans do change! Especially when the rug gets pulled out from beneath you.

I had to pick myself up and find my place in the world. Again!

Now I could get some things done around the house I had wanted to do. That lasted about two weeks.

I picked up temporary work and shuffled from job to job for a few years through an agency. One company wanted to hire me but couldn't, due to a hiring freeze. Others just wanted a temp but not to hire. I learned a lot along the way and tried taking computer classes to better my positions, but I was a woman over forty . . . And, well, my marketability was slim. A sign of the times. My husband and I talked about how the changing times of our society was either corporate or service. I had done factory work and worked my way into the office. It was a little late for me on the corporate ladder; although my experience opened doors for me working as a temp, I was still subject to layoffs. Computers were changing everything.

Early on, while I was a stay-at-home mom, I would be an office manager for my mom's tax business during the first four months of the year. After tax season, I turned a hobby into a craft business of my own, selling craft supplies and making custom macramé hangers, lamps, and tables. I even taught classes for kids and adults. I could make just about anything with macramé cord. I also did some cake decorating too! After the kids went off to elementary school, I took a job out of the home. Here I was, back home again.

And now, the kids were close to college age. How were we going to afford that?

So, what could I do that would allow me to control my own destiny? Really, I worked out of necessity, and now I wanted to do something for me. A few ideas floated through my head as I thought about starting up another business of my own. Or nursing, maybe? Always room for nurses. We discussed possibilities for me in personal care, but I wanted more, and then I decided on becoming a massage therapist. It seemed like the up-and-coming career move, and at that time, I was hoping I wasn't too late to get into it, as it was growing ever so popular. And there were all these corporate people needing massages due to hours sitting at desks in non-ergonomic chairs (who ever heard of that?) now more than ever, while staring into the one-eyed monster called computers.

> *I laugh as I hear most people in the offices today have two or more computers on their desks. How things have changed.* **You all need massages now more than ever!**

Sports enthusiasts: all teams had massage therapists. Even chiropractic was being recognized as being beneficial for good health and body alignment. They were bringing massage therapists into their offices. With the growing number of vehicles on the road, there are more car-accident victims, and those victims are turning to massage therapy for help. Even people with smaller home injuries recognize the benefits of massage.

There was a place for me as a massage therapist!

We would be retiring in a few years, and this I could do wherever we went.

This was something that had been on my mind for years before I was able to act upon it. Once I was able to follow that dream and become a massage therapist, it opened my eyes and mind to cultures of the world, and doors of other realities, I was not open to before.

I grew up on a farm with plants and animals and was close to nature in all my formative years. Massage has brought me back to that feeling of being grounded in nature.

It is a big part of my life to get my hands in the dirt, touch a tree, or bare feet in the grass. Or pet an animal!

* * *

I met my husband, Ernie, in the spring of 1969; it was love at first sight. I was seventeen, a senior in high school soon to graduate; he was twenty-three, serving in the Marine Corps, back from Vietnam. He was from Louisiana, and I was from Ohio. He left three days after we met, returning to Louisiana, but then returned later that year, in late July. He turned twenty-four in August, and I turned eighteen in October, and we were engaged on New Year's Eve! A new year, a new decade, a new beginning! We married the first day of spring, March 20, 1970, almost a year since we met.

We have always encouraged each other and our kids to think for themselves and encourage others.

When I told my family about my desire to become a massage therapist, they all encouraged me to go for it!

The wonders of the human body, and of people's spirit, never ceases to amaze me!

You just can't make it up!

This is my journey as I recall, from the beginning, my own experience of my first massage to some of the experiences of people I have had the pleasure of meeting and hearing and sharing stories with.

Perhaps if you have never had a massage and wonder what happens behind the closed doors, or if you are a fan of regular massages and know the benefit of them, I hope you will enjoy reading about some of my experiences from my point of view as the therapist.

Chapter 1
Emergency or Not?

"Lynn, I need your help," said the caller.

"Okay . . . what's your problem?"

"My name is Lola, and I got your name from a friend, and she recommended you. I'm having spasms across my back from overworking and driving and need a massage! I'm hurting so bad that I can't drive, and my husband will bring me."

"Perhaps you should go to the ER from the sound of things and get checked out first."

"We really don't believe or trust in doctors. We really want to do things holistically."

"I understand what you are saying, but you may need a picture"—meaning x-ray—"or muscle relaxer to help you. I am not a doctor, but I will see what I can do."

She was in my office in less than two hours. Her husband helped her in. As she stood there a minute, I studied her stance and movements and had an uneasy feeling. She was in her sixties, and I said again that I thought she should go to the ER.

"Please," she said. "We do NOT want to go to the hospital." We helped her into the other room for her to get on the massage table. Her husband stood next to the table the whole time. Everywhere I touched her, it hurt. She could hardly breathe.

I spoke to her in a slow, low voice while I worked on her. "You know, sometimes you have to trust the doctors. There is a place in this world for everybody. They can rule out things and give pain meds to help things along. I believe pain meds are good, but should only be temporary."

Her mid-back spasmed with each stroke I gave her and she cried out in pain. Finally, she quieted down and felt better from the soft strokes I applied to her. Mainly working her back and neck muscles calmed her down, so she rested. Then I worked her feet. The feet usually give me an indication or verification of what is going on in the body. Hmm . . . *Unsure*, I thought to myself, *do no harm and don't alarm!*

Her husband continued to stand next to the table, and I even asked him to take a step back so I could maneuver around her on the table. He watched everything I did with her arms and shoulders and expressed that he wanted to have one of my massages, as he liked what he saw. I had her lying faceup and facedown and, depending on her reactions, those turns were painful too.

After approximately ninety minutes, she couldn't thank me enough as she began to move to get up and dressed. However, she was still hurting as we sat down in my office.

"I feel seventy-five percent better. Thank you," she said.

"At this point, I'll take whatever improvement percentage I can get. But I must warn you, I am concerned that this is going to come back with a vengeance. Meaning, if you are feeling much better in the next twelve hours or tomorrow morning then I will be happy and maybe do a follow-up in a few days. But, if you feel the same or worse—as I fear—please get to the ER! Promise me that! You will need an X-ray or an MRI, or both. Protocol is an X-ray then MRI for most MDs."

"Well, right now I feel so much better." As she sighed with relief. "I want to make another appointment in a few days."

That appointment didn't happen! She sent me a text message the next day telling me she was in urgent care. They gave her pain meds and muscle relaxers and told her the same thing I did. If she didn't feel better by the next day, go to ER.

She was in my office Saturday afternoon, was at urgent care Sunday morning, and the ER Monday morning. She texted me again!

They admitted her into the hospital! A few days later, I texted her to ask of her progress. By the end of that week she was referred to five different doctors, undergoing tests to rule out fibromyalgia, inflammation, infection, pleurisy, and a collapsed lung. She said the technician was shocked as he looked at the CAT scan of her heart! They told her she had an aortic aneurysm with dissection!

Now I've heard of an aneurysm, and that sent chills through me. But I had to research the dissection and asked a few nurses and doctors about that. In other words, she was seriously ill. She has now deferred to doctors for treatment after that result. I check on her or she texts me messages on her progress every so often. I like to think I helped, in a small way, to get her the treatment she needed. Sometimes, you just know! But convincing the client is the challenge.

I've had the privilege of massaging everyday people!
Moms, dads, and kids. Oh, and sometimes the dog.

Medical doctors, chiropractors, and many nurses along my journey as a massage therapist. Business executives, professors, and teachers. Some still active or retired. Construction workers and sports people. People that are highly stressed or those with injuries. Also people before or after their surgeries. College students before or after exams. Young people and elderly.

I have urged some of my clients to see a doctor about possible skin cancer or perhaps a urinary infection, kidney stones, and even heart problems. Or any other condition I see or feel that needs attention by a physician.

Chapter 2
How It Began

March 1997—At age forty-five, I chose to step up and challenge myself to go back to school to become a massage therapist. I told my husband I wanted to do something to control my own destiny instead of working for someone else, making them money. He told me to go for it. I would be my own business. Maybe open my own massage day spa. A myriad of thoughts went through my mind. But let's get started first.

Could I learn something this new at my age? Was I too late? I'm a wife, a mom, and that would never change. Maybe getting into the health care business would open other doors. Maybe I could work in a hospital or doctor's office, or chiropractor's office. Chiropractors are recognized and accepted now for health care. They didn't used to be. We had to be careful who we talked to about chiropractors. My mom started seeing a chiropractor around 1961—I was ten years old—and I was cautioned not to say anything about it. He seemed very nice and even gave me an adjustment a few times. But he was a lifesaver for her. Massage? Well, that was unheard of back then, especially in the Midwest down on the farm.

I, myself, was a basket case after sitting at a desk as a

corporate desk jockey, with a phone at my ear—held there by my shoulder—punching buttons on a calculator, or typing newsletters. My shoulders ached endlessly, and even though I worked out regularly and saw a chiropractor often, it wasn't enough. But massage was just for the rich and famous, or after a golf game, as the movies would show. Or a luxury you do on vacation. Not what us Midwesterners do. But I knew it was for me. I could do good for people, help them feel better, and boy did it open my eyes.

Thinking of massage as a health benefit, not just relaxation, I thought about ways to help others realize it too. Perhaps pre-op to relax someone before surgery, and post-op for someone after surgery. Believe me, the last thing anyone wants after surgery is someone touching them or massaging. They are traumatized after an accident or surgery. But sometimes that's when they need it most. Lots of options floated through my head.

Being a massage therapist was something in the back of my mind ever since I heard of it. That seemed like a dream job, being in a spa setting, in a relaxing atmosphere. In the movies, it was usually men after a game of golf and a steam room wrapped in just a towel. White towels at that, always white in the movies. But then I saw an ad in our hometown newspaper:

Learn How to Massage Your Mate.
Couples Massage Class! $25 for 2 hours, bring a
large towel and a pillow!

Sponsored by a local massage therapist, the wife of a chiropractor in town.

I called and signed us up right away. This would give me

insight into this profession. The ad had an overwhelming response from couples around town. The class was held at her house with at least twenty couples showing up at her home, and we were in the living room, dining room, and kitchen—anywhere we could fit. She was overwhelmed at the response and told us that many people called but she didn't expect this many to show up. Making the best of the situation, she proceeded to explain how to massage the neck and shoulders while laying on a towel on the floor with pillows under the head or knees. The class ended up lasting four hours into the evening.

My husband and a few others in this introductory class didn't seem to grasp the idea at all, but it really sparked my interest. She tried to explain a few techniques, and we would take turns practicing on each other. There were a couple of massage therapist assistants there also to help oversee the couples as we tried to massage each other. Being on our hands and knees on the floor was very challenging for everyone. The interest was there but comfort was not.

Overall, it was an introduction to massage in our town that was not readily accepted. One of the assistants massaged my shoulders, and I knew this was for me and what I needed. My husband tried to do the massaging she instructed, but he just didn't have the touch. After four hours, we were handed a folder with instruction sheets to take home and practice on each other. We tried some of the massage techniques days later, a time or two on the floor at my insistence, but I was not able to convince my husband to reciprocate much at all. He loved it and was willing to let me work on him. But I ached from daily hours of desk work and housework and was totally ignorant of the real health benefits of massage. Like anything else, some people are not cut out to do massages.

Like in my massage practice today, people come to me because of a need and wish they could get their spouse to help with their aches and pains, but as most couples find out, one or the other likes to massage and the other one does not. Some people can and others can't, or won't. And some just don't have the touch or interest to do so.

Occasionally, I'll invite a client for a massage session with their spouse or child to teach a few techniques to them. Or they will ask if their spouse can come along to watch or take notes.

My son Lee, around age thirteen, would ask me to massage his legs before going to bed because they ached. He was athletic in high school and played football, wrestling, and softball during the summer and was in the marching band. Thinking he was just sore, I would rub his legs not knowing what I was doing felt uncomfortable. I asked our chiropractor for his opinion on why my son's legs hurt so much and why the pain occurred mostly at night.

Dr. H. said, "Look at him, he's a growing boy—six feet tall! Literally *growing* pains!"

"Of course I know he's growing, I have to feed him!" was my remark.

"Kids often get growing pains during their teen years because they are growing so fast. The long bones like the ones in the legs will ache as they lengthen and feel painful. Especially at night during restful, inactive time. As the body relaxes, the bones grow."

He then told me, "Let me show you a little bit about massage so you can help him. I don't want you to bring him to me every week for something you can do. The main thing you must remember about massage is that you always move toward the venous flow which is the superficial blood flow. Start at the bottom and work toward the heart. That is venous blood flow, always toward the heart."

My first massage lesson was by Dr. H., our chiropractor around 1987.

The nearest Massage School for me was eighty miles away. That was a long way for me to go and was out of the question: I was working full time, a wife, and mom of two school-age kids. The classes were full time during the day, and I couldn't quit my life to go to school full time! I had to shelf the idea at that time.

But years later, in the spring of 1997, I was working temporary jobs, and the school was offering night classes. I called and got a packet of forms. One was an application to the Ohio State Medical Board for a license to go to massage therapy school, and one was an application to apply to the school. With the application, I had to write an essay about why I wanted to do massage therapy, plus get three sponsors to sign a consent form agreeing that I would be a good person for massage. Then I had to have three massages myself, from three different massage therapists, and have them sign papers verifying I had received a massage from them. Until then, I never had a full-body, one-hour massage from anyone. I wanted to do massage but had not experienced a full-body massage myself.

There were only a couple massage therapists in my hometown, and they didn't offer student massages. After making a few phone calls, I had my first massage from a professional, licensed massage therapist near Troy, Ohio.

My First Full-Body Massage!

My appointment was ten a.m., and I arrived on time and introduced myself to the lady. It was a nice place, similar to a resort out in the country. I was the only person there. She introduced herself and said she was a nurse.

The place was very clean, and new, and elegant for a country setting. She led me to a dressing room, and asked me to undress to my comfort level, put on a robe, and go through the door to the massage room and get on the table. I took off everything but my underwear, slipped on the white robe, and went across the hall to the massage room, where it felt exposed to the outside by a large patio door overlooking a large, manicured yard. Beyond that was a large, open field I could see out over for miles. I took off the robe, laid it on a chair, and slipped under the sheet on the massage table, face up.

She then came in to begin the massage. We chatted a bit about me wanting to be a massage therapist myself, and as she started to massage me, tears flooded my eyes the whole time. I couldn't stop my eyes from tearing. I apologized for the teary eyes. I wasn't scared or hurt; I had never let anyone into my personal space before. Yes, I am a wife and a mother, but never have I let anyone in my personal space touch me all over, and the emotional release of it was overwhelming.

I won't forget that when someone new comes to see me.

Although massage therapy has become more popular and well known in the past twenty years, that first experience can be a bit traumatic.

I wear scrubs most of the time while I do massages because it helps give the feeling of being a health care provider to put people at ease—A uniform! It helps to look like a licensed professional so they feel they are in good hands.

When I got all my papers together, I sent in the application, along with application fees, and was notified to come for an interview along with my husband. He had to give consent for me to attend the school. It was a counseling session for both of us to make sure this profession would not be problematic for our marriage. Ernie told the school officials it was my decision, and he was all for it since I wanted it. We interviewed separately and together, and I was accepted that day but missed getting into the spring class by two weeks. I had hoped the administrator would let me start and make up the two weeks so I could get started right away but was denied. I would have to wait six months until fall classes started. I was crushed!

That was the last time I was at that school.

Chapter 3
Things Happen for a Reason!

Don't ever doubt that!

During late summer, I discovered a new massage school had opened nearer to me in Dayton. Spring classes had been underway, and the school was planning for the fall semester. What a savings it would be for me to get into this school and be forty miles closer than the other school. I sent in an application. It cost me the application fees but what a savings on the travel expense. I had already applied and gotten my license from the Ohio State Medical Board that is required for massage therapy schools in Ohio. That entailed an extensive background check to determine I was not a mental case, felon, or a pedophile.

Again, we were contacted for another interview, again with husband, but since I had an acceptance certificate from the previous school located near Cincinnati, we didn't have to go through the whole interview. After all, I was going to touch bodies of all types—color, shape, age, gender, size, religion, famous, healthy, ill, etc. They had to get his response on whether or not it would interfere with our marriage. He was all in. It was my decision. He thought it would be good for me and encouraged it. I was working as a full-time temp for another corporation at the time and was able to pay monthly installments to the school without having to take out a loan. Ernie was also thinking about retirement in a few years, and this could be something I could do anywhere we went—have massage table, will travel. Hey, that was another option! All about options these days!

I was accepted to the Dayton School of Medical Massage (DSMM)!

When I announced to my mother that I was going to school to study massage therapy, she was mortified. She told me I couldn't do that because I was a "married woman with children!" I looked at her with a blank look, rethinking what I had just said to make sure she didn't misunderstand me. You see, in her mind that meant I was going to be a professional prostitute.

The stigma of massage parlors was still something I had to overcome, especially in the Midwest. There are many giggles, snickers, raised eyebrows, and "oh's?" So, I'm careful not to say massage parlor because of the history associated with it. I want to be known as a professional licensed massage therapist—LMT.

Summer came and went, and we worked to keep the family going. I tried to brush up on reading and meditation while the excitement about going back to school built up. Lee was living in Bowling Green, Ohio, and Elton was at Ohio State, getting back into the routine of classes after summer break. As September was fading, the first day of class was approaching on a Monday.

We received a call . . . that left us stunned!

Left on the answering machine Sunday afternoon,

September 28, a message that Ernie's mom and dad were involved in an automobile accident. They were traveling from North Carolina to Louisiana on I-20 in Meridian, Mississippi, and my father-in-law was killed. Surely it had to be a mistake. But the bad news was soon verified.

I have a motto: "You do what you have to do when you have to do it!"

When confronted with something unexpected, you have to face the challenge.

"Look," I told my husband. "It will take a day or two to get the kids here. You fly on down to Louisiana to help with arrangements. Your mom is in the hospital in Mississippi. Your sisters are headed there to get her." Ernie has six sisters and three brothers. They lived in South Carolina, Louisiana, Ohio, and Texas.

"The funeral for your dad won't be until the end of the week in Coushatta, depending on how your mom is. I cannot miss my first day of class. First day of introductions! I need to get excused from work and the boys need to get excused from their work and school, and get home. The boys and I will drive down Wednesday night and be there Thursday."

My first day of massage class was Monday night, beginning at six p.m. till eleven p.m., with a thirty-minute lunch break. My first anatomy class was Wednesday at the same time.

I got approval from my work to take bereavement leave, and I got off at 3:30, was home by four, changed clothes, and drove to the first night class myself. On Wednesday, I met with classmates to carpool with that night. My sons picked me up from school that Wednesday night after class, and I crawled into the back seat of that vehicle at eleven p.m. and let them drive.

"Wake me up if you need me." I was exhausted, and

we drove all night to Louisiana, taking turns driving. One thousand miles with just road maps and signs from Dayton, Ohio, to Coushatta, Louisiana. It was a familiar trip but different this time, as it was one for duty, not pleasure. After the funeral, we would all be back together for the drive home with our immediate family to help each other heal from a devastating loss.

The First Massage Class

Eighteen months sounds like an eternity in the beginning. I settled into a routine of driving to night classes twice a week and making time to study every day. I was so blessed and fortunate to carpool with two other women who lived north of me. We would meet at a restaurant parking lot near Interstate 75 and take turns driving each week. From that point, it was an hour and a half to school because of traffic, and about forty-five minutes to an hour coming back. It was like having our own study group on the way to class, and sometimes we wouldn't get home until almost midnight, especially on cold, snowy, winter evenings. I considered myself lucky as we drove into the parking lot where we met each night, as the other women still had almost another hour to get to their homes. For me, it was twenty minutes.

On the first day of massage class, about forty-five people showed up, and we all made introductions.

The average age was about forty-three. There were a couple of eighteen-year-olds just out of high school, and a twenty-something gal who described herself as an escort (eyebrows raised at that one). A young man in his mid-twenties, who already worked for a chiropractor and was being paid to study massage to get his license. A few people were in their thirties, but most, like me, were in their forties. One small-statured man said he was a former

Marine and openly gay. One woman was from a South American country and her English was poor.

What I'm trying to say is the variety of people in that first day of class was eye-opening; it was an incredibly diverse group. We all talked a bit about ourselves and why we wanted to do massage therapy. Most of us chose the field because massage therapists helped us recover after an injury. We had a couple of students who were interested in infant massage, and I discovered there are many different modalities of massage. We all had a different perspective of what massage could be. As I said, many in that room that day were there because they saw a need to help others overcome injuries or repetitive-use injuries on the job.

I can also say that anyone who thinks it is easy to be in a room with dim lighting and soft music, as you stand over someone, rubbing him or her with oil or lotion, does not know what massage is.

That type of massage is what we call "Fluff and Buff."

That is not what most people want. And it quickly becomes a lot more work than they bargained for. The younger ones in the class, or those looking for a profession that they thought would be easy work and easy money, soon dropped out.

The Second Massage Class . . .

. . . Was all about anatomy and physiology. My medical book cost well over $450 back then, and we studied the whole body inside and out. After all, it is a medical massage school, and it is necessary to know about the human body. This was the hardest part of the classes for me. I carried two briefcases—one for massage class and one for anatomy class—each week. Several had already dropped out by the second class.

Chapter 4
The Heart of Massage

The Dayton School of Medical Massage not only taught about the techniques of massage, but also anatomy, physiology, and the history of massage. *The Art of Massage* was the first book of massage written in the United States, by John Harvey Kellogg in 1895, and was one of our class study guides. Some of the findings in this book have since been proven untrue, such as "massage can cure baldness," but the book details the basic massage techniques that have been handed down through time.

The origin of massage, according to Kellogg, dates back three thousand years to ancient China. Massage in the East was the original, hands-on medicine. Ancient Chinese massage was exclusively performed by blind men due to their acute, sensory skill of touch. Massage continued through the centuries with oils and potions to sustain good health.

The negative stigma of massage parlors came along after the European wars. Children in orphanages or convents were out on their own, usually by age sixteen. Orphan girls or unmarried women needed to be taught a trade. Boys could go into the army or work, easily. Nursing was said to be too expensive to teach girls if they didn't want to stay in a convent. Young women were taught to be wives, cooks, caregivers, servants or maids, or midwives. So, it was decided to teach them to be masseuses. It was not as costly as nursing school, and it would give girls an occupation that was acceptable.

That approach turned disastrous. Massage parlors morphed into brothels which quickly became very popular among men. This led to the bad reputation given to massages and massage parlors that has taken us two hundred years to overcome. That's why my mother had such a reaction when I introduced to her the notion that I was going to study massage therapy.

Even today, massage businesses are being shut down for elicit practices of sexual behavior. We Americans are taught to drape our clients during massages to keep modesty and boundaries between therapist and client. It is unlawful here in America to touch people in the genital area during massages, and I don't even want to go there, but I've been asked, bribed, and insulted to do so.

> *I was having a pedicure at a Vietnamese-owned establishment; the girls were chatting among themselves in their language. Knowing I was a massage therapist, one of the ladies that spoke English asked me, "Do you do whole body? The other girls ask me to ask you."*
>
> *I had a feeling of what she was asking.*
>
> *"Whole body as in everywhere, including men's penises?" I asked.*
>
> *"Yes."*
>
> *"Oh heavens, no," I replied with a bit of disgust, wrinkling my nose at the thought. She relayed what I said to the others and they laughed and snickered among themselves.*

I watched their reaction to my answer, and then she replied, "In our country, it is okay!"

I thought for a moment. Then replied, "One, it is unlawful here in the States. Which I'm thankful for. Two, I don't even want to go there. A guy can take care of himself elsewhere. We are here for health benefits not sexual favors. I don't want to go there for some guy, and my husband wouldn't like it either."

They kind of talked about it, and I noticed a serious look and wondered if they saw my point of view. But the exchange opened my eyes about some of the beliefs of other countries. They are a different culture than ours, and we should be understanding and have mutual respect that causes no harm to anyone. A sexual favor, on the other hand, is unlawful here in the States. They laughed at our outlook on that philosophy, and I thought it disgusting. The subject never came up again, but I can understand why so many establishments get raided or shut down.

That's Why I Prefer to Do Therapeutic Massage!

Numerous times, I've gotten looks and snickers from people when they learn I am a massage therapist. They wonder what goes on behind closed doors. I welcome questions from anyone who wants to be serious about my occupation.

Chapter 5
We Learn
from Each Other

Time flies when you're having fun or keeping busy. About eight months into the eighteen months of classes, I was making flash cards at home on my computer so I could have them with me during the day and on breaks to study. Learning names of muscles and innervations and lots of anatomy and physiology was the most difficult for me. So, flash cards were extremely helpful. I made them myself to help me learn and retain the information. The women I worked with learned too, as they would help me study during breaks.

I developed a case of tendinitis in my elbow, also known as tennis elbow, from overworking my right arm using the mouse and typing so much day and night.

Tendonitis: inflammation of a tendon.

I almost had to drop out of class. I saw my doctor, and he injected my elbow with a cortisone shot, which was very painful. It relieved the pain for a couple of weeks.

After the third injection in about four months, he informed me that was the limit for a year. My elbow hurt, and I had it in a sling and couldn't lift a glass of water. I was attending classes but couldn't do massage practice. After talking with one of my instructors, I asked if I had to drop out or could she do something to help me. She only replied that it would be my decision should I decide to drop out. When another classmate, Susie, asked me if she could look at my elbow, I was grateful for any help she could provide. After all, we were here to learn how to help people.

"This may hurt some," she told me.

"It couldn't hurt any worse than the injections or more than it already does," I replied.

She maneuvered her finger between the two bones in my elbow—I could tell you the names of the bones: ulnar and olecranon. I know that now. Anyway, there is a small tendon between those two bones, and she got the tip or her finger in between those two bones and released that tendon. And by massaging it, the pain disbursed, releasing it.

Incredible, I had learned something from a fellow student that I have since used in my own practice. Also, I learned how to do it for myself, so when it flares up, I can release it on my own. I have had clients with the same problem and have shown them and others how to help themselves!

I must say, sometimes it doesn't work for everybody, I'm glad when it does.

My interest in learning the art of massage was to see where it took me.

Susie usually sat in front of me during lectures, and numerous times when the instructor would ask a question, I would mutter the answer under my breath, and she would hold up her hand and give the answer, and then turn her head slightly my way and say, "thank you." I would smile at her and nod. Later, she asked, "Why didn't you answer these questions? You always know the answer."

I would say, "You answered, what's the difference?"

She was a nice woman in her early forties with a teenage daughter, as I recall. She was taking the course because she wanted to be a preemie infant massage therapist. I didn't know then that people did that. She and another woman attended a seminar about baby and infant massage before we graduated from this class. They also shared their experiences with our class. It was exciting to be so blessed to share experiences with these classmates.

One of my carpool companions became pregnant during the last nine months of class, so we as a class had the privilege of experiencing her pregnancy with her, and she received lots of attention as we learned about pregnancy massage.

Unfortunately, about a year after we graduated, I heard that Susie died suddenly from an aneurysm, I think. But whatever it was, I was saddened at the loss.

* * *

Studying every day, minimally four hours a day, and attending night classes twice a week became a routine for that eighteen months. Nearly every class began with a test on what we learned the week, or weeks, before.

Our anatomy/physiology instructor was a young pre-med student, the same age as my son, who already had four years of anatomy and physiology and was very qualified to teach a bunch of "wannabe" massage therapists.

He really knew his anatomy. Sometimes, he would ask class members to help him with his education by asking for volunteers to let him draw blood for practice or experimentation. I shied away from that myself. Getting stuck by an amateur didn't appeal to me, but I liked to watch occasionally. The faces some of the others made was a bit amusing. I was a little disappointed we didn't get to do cadaver study, but we did watch cadaver videos.

The anatomy/physiology textbook we studied had two chapters devoted to just muscles. We spent six weeks or more on those two chapters, and that didn't seem like enough at the time, but we plowed our way through those chapters, learning to pronounce, spell, and know where those muscles were and what they did. I had study groups come to my house some evenings or weekend days, and we quizzed ourselves on them. My husband sometimes was our practice body on the table when we needed one. He loved that. There was never a lack of volunteers when you needed a body to practice on.

"Eight hundred and fifty-five approximate muscles in the human body, most of them in pairs." I took that quote from a movie I saw somewhere some time ago. It was a robot explaining about human anatomy, and I heard it so many times that I felt it appropriate to use whenever someone asks me. Note: 855 approximate muscles! Not everyone has all of those. Questions were asked about that. The answer is in our DNA.

There is so much more to massaging than knowing muscles. We studied anatomy from conception—the beginning of the human body like atoms form cells, cells form tissues, tissues form organs, organs form systems, and systems make us a whole body.

The eleven systems of the body are: skeletal, nervous, circulatory, lymphatic, muscular, integumentary, endocrine, respiratory, digestive, urinary, and reproductive.

Everything usually comes in even numbers. It mystified me that we would have only eleven systems.

It has now come to be recognized that another system called fascia does exist, which makes perfect sense as a massage therapist, but is still controversial to some medical practitioners. So, that saga continues.

"I am not a doctor." I say that a lot when people ask me questions about anatomy and health. As a mom and massage therapist, continuing education classes and life itself rewards us with life learning experiences. Wisdom is grand. And I learn from the experiences of my clientele too.

Massage therapists need to know how to describe the body like a road map for a doctor when necessary. It gives us a better understanding of what is located where and what is relevant, and whether we're talking about superficial, deep, or sagittal planes, frontal or superior, and many more when describing an area of the body.

This is not intended to be an anatomy lesson, but I'm trying to let you know that learning massage therapy is a great deal of work. And what we learned in the classroom helped give us confidence when we graduated. But little did we really know, basics, and the rest, were up to us.

Oh, and this is a medical massage school. I enjoyed the whole process and was willing to endure. The time flew by fast. I struggled with tests all the way through. I passed most of my tests by narrow margins as I had a phobia of testing. My study groups were amazed that I struggled, because in groups and class, I didn't have any problems. I choked when taking tests.

Midway through the classes, students were required to do twenty hours of clinicals by offering massages to the public. That way we got hands-on practice. People came in for student massages at half of the going rate.

First Assignments

One of my first assignments was a young woman who was given a gift certificate from a friend. We were both nervous as it was her first massage ever, and she was embarrassed at being there. I, too, was nervous and unsure of techniques and timing. My first massages were mixed with uncertainty. We went into the treatment room, and she repeatedly told me she didn't want to do this, but her sister insisted. She decided that all she wanted me to do was her neck and shoulders, and that's all! So, she didn't want to get undressed or anything, but she took off her shirt and kept on her undies, shorts, and socks. As I began massaging her arms, shoulders, and neck, she began to relax.

"Just my neck and shoulders, and I'll be out of here," she said again.

"Are you sure?"

"Well, that sure feels good," she said.

"I would like to do your feet also, if you want?" I asked.

"Well, just my feet, please. This feels really good. Just my feet and I'll be out of here."

Then she sat up, and asked if I would do her legs. "I wasn't going to, but it feels really good, so would you do my legs?"

"Looks like we are going to use up that whole hour you got a gift for."

By then, she was hooked. She could not give it up! I had won her over to the gift of massage. I asked her to turn over, and I finished by massaging her back as well as I could. And she didn't want to leave.

I volunteered to do extra clinicals to help get extra credit, just in case I needed it.

A young married couple came in as an anniversary present for each other, and I was assigned to the young man. During clinicals, we leave the doors slightly open for safety reasons when in sessions with the opposite sex.

As we introduced ourselves, the young man made it clear he didn't want to be there. The couple were in their midtwenties, but she had insisted they were going to do this. He was looking at some brochures and asked if he could bring some of them with him to read while getting his massage, as he would be bored. The other student therapist started to say something, but I quickly stated, "Of course, if you want reading material! The lights will be dim, but please bring it with you. Just in case."

He quickly found out he didn't want reading material. I was glad the door was open. As I massaged him, he was awestruck. When I massaged his back, he was moaning and groaning so loud, I expected—maybe even hoped—someone would check on us to make sure it was all legitimate. When I finished, he looked like a rag doll walking out of the room. I handed him his brochures to take home, and he smiled sheepishly. He wanted to tip, but we were not allowed to accept them. He said he loved the massage and would definitely be back.

Those clinical hours helped build my confidence.

At Home

My dad became my advocate. He had never heard of massage until I explained it to him. I asked him to give it a try and let me practice on him, and he couldn't believe how good it made him feel. He was having some health issues with circulation, and he became my weekly regular volunteer. Although as my father, he would not undress for me. He would only take off his shirt for me to work his arms, neck, and shoulders.

It helped him sleep better. Later, I helped him recover

from a heart bypass surgery when he developed thoracic outlet syndrome.

How I wish I had more experience back then to help him more. The old saying "if I only knew back then what I know now!" comes to mind.

* * *

By the end of the eighteen months, seventeen of us made it to graduation in the spring of 1999. I had a massage table for class that was mandatory for us to purchase for training, but this was going to be my livelihood. Carrying a massage table to and from class was cumbersome but we quickly got used to it. After looking at various tables and comparing notes with other classmates, I decided to invest in a better table. My research took me to the Golden Ratio massage table made in Montana, which was designed for Thai massage because it would fold out and lay flat on the floor. I insisted on adding extra padding and rounded corners. The extra cost was worth it! I had lots of other modalities in mind to learn and expected it to last a long time.

I'm still using that table today, twenty years later!

My son and daughter-in-law attended my graduation ceremony, which was special. They both had graduated from college the year before and thought it was important to see their mother graduate from school also. Ernie and I had moved to Georgia prior to my graduation, but he was working so he didn't attend.

I bought myself a gold ankle bracelet as a graduation gift to myself and told Ernie it was from him. He gladly agreed!

Chapter 6
Now the Real Education Begins!

Not long after graduation, I began researching other types (modalities) of massage. I wanted to learn reflexology (massage of hands and feet). We had touched very little on that subject in school, but I was fascinated by it. Feet relate to every other part of the body. How can that be? I knew I had so much more to learn and questions to be answered.

Ernie encouraged me to speak in medical terms whenever I could so I would retain the terms. As with any language, if you don't use it, you will forget. People are always impressed when you use medical terms, and then you can explain it if necessary. Quite frequently, a client will come in with a name of a muscle written on a piece of paper from a doctor asking if I know what and where it is. Without hesitation and with confidence, I can confirm that I do and pronounce it too! Everyone learns something. Back to body roadmap. If you speak of quads and hamstrings, that is definitive rather than just saying leg or thigh.

A client, came in one day with certain leg pain,

trying to describe her problem. Then I repeated by saying "IT bands and tensor fasciae latae right side to the lateral malleolus."

She looked at me with wide open eyes as she was starting to undress and said, "Oh, I love it when you talk medical terms to me!" We both laughed at the sound of it.

I eventually wanted to learn how to do Thai massage if I could find the right teacher. In the meantime, I needed to learn more about sports massage. That seemed more important at this time, and what most people wanted. That and "deep tissue."

Deep tissue can be hard on a practitioner who hasn't had proper training and body mechanics. We can hurt ourselves easy and quick without using proper movements. I discovered that most people doing massage as an occupation only last about seven years after graduation. That number is now approximately four years. Although, it looks and sounds easy, it is not.

One could either work at a spa, for a sports team, event, or a cruise ship. Those all sound glamorous, but the work is very hard. Nowadays, we see franchises opening in cities and towns, malls, shopping centers, and airports. These are good if a massage therapist doesn't want the burden of trying to market him or herself as a business and can walk in and start working somewhere. We now have more massage schools and facilities for us massage professionals.

When you get a massage therapy license, you are in a database that lists those active and inactive for that state. When I graduated from massage school in Ohio, that gave me a certification as a massage therapist, not a license. We moved to Georgia and that state didn't require a license, therefore I didn't have one. Just a certification. At that time, I was a certified massage therapist.

Ernie retired from the corporate world, and we decided to move somewhere with warmer weather. We wanted to be closer to his family that lived in Louisiana—about a day's drive—and yet be close enough to mine for a day's drive.

We took up residence near a resort in North Georgia, and that gave me a chance to hone my new skill. Most of the clientele were weekenders or vacationers touring the North Georgia area. Hiking the mountains was a big thing, plus there were a lot of tourist places like the Appalachian Trail and Amicalola Falls, the German village of Helen, Dahlonega's gold mines where the first US gold rush happened, and the famous Trail of Tears of Cherokee Indians. Oh, and Thunder Road Racing Museum in Dawsonville with the Moonshine Still as well as Lake Lanier. These places were all north of Atlanta, where visitors drove in or flew in on business, vacation, or layovers. Most visitors at the resort would lie around the pool and would keep me busy. The cabana next to the pool was my private space for massage. It was a screened room that was close to activity without being too secluded. I met new people almost every weekend throughout the summer months. My husband would show tourists around and make sure to point out the massage therapist on staff: *me!*

> *One thing about resort or spa work is that you have the opportunity to meet lots of different people with lots of ideas, expectations, or speculations. The majority of these people you rarely see twice, unless they are local or visit often to become regular.*

One Saturday, I was sitting at my desk writing SOAP notes, with my back turned to the door of the cabana, when a fellow came in the screen door and just stood there. I glanced up quickly to acknowledge the gentleman and asked him to have a seat and said I'd be right with him. He sat down on the massage table opposite me, facing the other direction. Still with my back to him, I felt his apprehensiveness as I turned around and stood up to walk around the table to give him my full attention. He had a very serious look on his face as I started to ask him his name, then I noticed he had a prosthetic leg to the knee.

"Oh, wow!" I said with amazement and enthusiasm. "You have a prosthesis!" I felt his nervousness and was trying to put him at ease. We both had to read the other's body language about this.

"Do you have a problem with that?" he asked with a sullen look. I guess he thought I might ask him to leave or go screaming out of the room. I was thinking what luck for me to have a new experience working with an amputee!

"I don't. Do you?" I asked with hesitation. "Are you going to leave that on or take it off?" I asked him as he relaxed a little bit.

"Can I?" he asked with this big Grinch grin—ear to ear smile—on his face! I mean this guy lit up!

"Of course! You do want me to massage around your stump, don't you?"

It looked like he couldn't get his prosthesis off fast enough. I really made this man's day as he was unstrapping it from his knee.

"Okay, just let me know what, if anything, I can do for you, and can I ask questions about it without offending you?" I said as we began.

"This is great!" he said. "You can't hurt it, and feel free

to ask anything." He handed me the artificial leg and I laid it aside on a chair.

That was my first amputee. I was most curious about phantom pain and how everything felt after losing the leg itself. He answered my questions as directly as I asked them, without hesitations. He was a happy camper that I didn't find his disfigurement disgusting. I didn't treat him special or different, but ordinary. That was refreshing for him. We talked and laughed, and he asked me for a hug after the hour. He left all smiles, and said he felt great.

I never saw him again.

But when I think of him, I smile.

* * *

There was another gentleman that summer who came to me every Saturday for six consecutive Saturdays because he had a bad sciatica problem. He was in such pain and his doctor told him massage was best, and he didn't know anyone else, so I worked with him, stretching his hamstrings those Saturdays as he winced in pain but a good kind of hurt. The last Saturday I saw him, he stepped into the screened room, the screen door closing behind him with a light bang, and for the first time that summer, he had a big smile on his face. As I looked at him, I said, "Oh! YOU are pain free!"

"Yes! And I have you to thank for it! Now I want a massage that I can enjoy. And I can't thank you enough."

"Well, I appreciate that, but I just do the best I know how. Glad I could help."

I don't remember seeing him again after that summer.

Massage Therapists Need Massages Too!

I learned a lot those first years in Georgia. I often wondered what was going on back in corporate America. The wheels of fate turned dramatically and changed our lives. I met other massage therapists along the way. I recall one person who asked me where I went to school and how long I had been practicing. I proudly said a couple of years, and she told me I was still a baby and had lots to learn. I took offense to it at first. I was in my late forties and had changed my life from corporate America, gone back to school, and was hungry to learn and really liked what I was doing. But she was seasoned. After I massaged her, she said she was very impressed with my knowledge and technique. She even asked if she could borrow a couple of moves I used on her. That was a high compliment from a peer. Also, working with different people on a daily basis opened my senses deeper than ever and opened my eyes to opportunities for learning about different cultures, how people feel and think, and even skin textures. Beliefs and disbeliefs. Energies—massage is all about the energy we feel and how we connect with each other, and I don't mean physical touch alone.

Weekends were always busy, with people sometimes coming in on Thursday evening or Friday afternoons. My busiest days were weekends, massaging four or five clients on Fridays, six or seven clients on Saturdays, and winding down on Sundays, usually three or four and a few carryovers on Monday—one or two. On any weekend, I was massaging an average of fifteen people. Those numbers would increase when it rained. Since people couldn't lounge at the pool, they would get a massage.

One weekend a group of local friends got together and purchased a gift certificate for a massage therapist friend of theirs for her birthday. She lived and worked nearby.

"After all," they said, "what better gift for a massage therapist than a massage that she can't give to herself?"

I was glad to meet her, and the massage went very well. Afterward, she asked me how long it had been since I had a massage.

"Oh. Not since I graduated from massage school," I said to her.

"You need a massage, and I'd like to treat you to a massage at my office," she prompted.

"Oh no, you don't need to do that. This is your birthday gift."

"No!" she insisted. "I want you to come to my office next week. I'll set up a time next week on your day off, and you come meet with me. Not taking no for an answer!" She wrote down an address and instructions to the chiropractic office where she worked and handed me the note.

"Well, I guess I will take you up on your offer. Thank you." I handed her my card with my home phone number (cell phones were not handy at that time. Not everyone had one, and reception in the mountains was poor.).

She called me the following Monday after she had returned to her office with a time and day for me to see her.

The following Tuesday morning, I drove to Roswell and met with Carolyne at her office and had one of the best massages ever. It had been nearly a year since I had a massage, and I realized, as she worked me over for almost two hours of deep tissue, how much I had been taking on from others. She knew that of me. And she knew from experience that I was not channeling negative energy away but was taking it on.

A few weeks earlier, I experienced a very busy weekend massaging seven people a day Friday, Saturday, and Sunday, and by Monday, I was hurting and felt like I needed help, so I turned to a chiropractic adjustment. I could hardly get out of bed; I was so beat and mentioned to my chiropractor that everyone I worked on that weekend had some kind of pain or injury.

"Yes," he said, "and they all felt better as you took their pain onto yourself. You have to learn not to do that, or you have to find a way to channel it. People will do that to you if you let it. And it will harm you."

Carolyne was telling me the same thing as she worked the toxins from my muscles, and she could feel the knots I was building up. It hurt but it was good hurt.

> That's one reason massage therapists can only do this work for a few years before they burn out. You must find what works for you to channel negativity away.
>
> Another cause for burnout is improper body mechanics. If a therapist gets sloppy with stance and movements while working on a body, it will cause injury or problems for their own body.

I liked her massage room, music, and her expert hands. I heard many times that she was good and had to agree. I had lots to learn, I knew, but was not intimidated. I hadn't had a massage since leaving school and wanted to learn from this experience.

"I want you to feel how you make other people feel," she said.

When she finished, after two hours, I felt lethargic and sleepy and had difficulty driving the thirty minutes back home, trying to stay awake. I drank water all the way home, partly to stay awake and I was detoxing and dehydrated.

As soon as I got home, I pulled off my shoes and top layer of clothes and slipped into bed under the sheet in my underwear and fell asleep. I stayed there all day, only getting up for water and to use the bathroom throughout the day. Eating was out of the question. Ernie came in for dinner, saw I was in bed, and asked if I was all right. I said yes but fell back to sleep. He fixed his own dinner that night. I slept nearly twenty hours.

The next morning when I woke up, I jumped up feeling like a super woman! As I stood up and took a step, I felt weightless and looked down at my feet to see if they were touching the floor. What an incredible feeling of weightlessness and strength I felt. I wish I had stepped on the scale, but I didn't think of it then and that might have intervened with my euphoria. I ate light that first day and was famished by the second morning. I touched the back of my neck a little and felt tender across my shoulders and asked Ernie if my shoulders were bruised because it was sore to the touch.

Deep tissue massage can cause you to feel bruised but not necessarily be bruised. I don't like bruising people, but it can happen sometimes.

The next three days were like that! I felt like I was walking on air, and within three days, the air under my feet became less and less, getting back to normal again.

Detoxing

Many clients throughout my years tell me they felt taller or like they walking on air after a massage. Or just the opposite, like they were sleepy and needed to go to sleep. I've also had clients get flu or flu-like symptoms, and this is all due to detoxing. A massage can give you a myriad of feelings or symptoms. Feeling dizzy after a massage is also common!

Do what your body or heart is telling you!

This one massage taught me more than I could have imagined, and it helped me understand what I do for others. The results can be very different for each person or each massage. I recall someone saying to me she liked coming to me because each massage was different and "you like what you do, and it shows."

That one massage renewed my spirits for sure. And I never forgot it!

Chapter 7
Meet in the Middle!

The North Georgia Mountains have so much history, and those summers were good for me to learn my new skill. Some folks didn't want to accept me right away because I was from up north, Yankee country, Ohio. When Ernie and I first met, we were from different cultures. He was from Louisiana and I was from Ohio, and always, the first question asked by everyone was: "How did you both meet?"

The question by us is: "Do you want the condensed version? Otherwise it's a long story."

The short version is our brothers met in Vietnam. They were different branches of the service. Ernie and his brother were Marines. His brother Ronald was in close proximity to my brother, a Navy Seabee, and they became friends. Since both had sisters, they traded their addresses. My brother James got home from Vietnam and went to visit the family of the friend he met from Louisiana, and shortly after, married one of the sisters. Then when Ernie was coming home from his tour in Vietnam, he swung by, about three hundred miles out of his way home, to visit his sister, who married this Ohio Yankee dude. And that's when we met. It was a lot more complicated than this at the time. But that's the condensed version.

Him being a southerner helped ease the transition for me when we moved to North Georgia. Because Ernie was a southern boy, he fit right in. Things have changed dramatically since those days. Cultural differences. But it helped to understand why people are the way they are. It's like rival teams. The North versus the South. East versus West.

Ernie had similar findings when he moved to Ohio and we got married. He had to understand our ways. As I say jokingly, "I had to 'learn' him English." I know the proper word is "teach." He would often say things like "carry me to town." I said, "I will drive you, but I won't carry you," with a laugh.

My dad had a hard time accepting this Marine, the oldest of ten siblings. He feared I would be forever barefoot and pregnant by this southern boy! Ernie's dad had a hard time accepting the fact he was marrying a Yankee!

We are Americans first, but we had our cultural differences.

Now that we are in a resort in North Georgia, we see a large mix and blend of people that come in from all over the world. People have become so mobile all over the world.

Chapter 8
A Few Stories

Camping

A large motor coach came into the camping area of the resort and stayed for a month one summer. It was hard to call it camping with such a fine set of wheels, but most campers we had the pleasure of meeting were especially friendly and that made the world special. The gentleman and his wife who drove this coach were fond of massages, especially after a long day's drive. The husband liked my massages and came more frequently, about twice a week while at the resort.

He was a former race car driver and had been in a three-car, fiery crash during a race, and was severely scarred over his body. He had been given a slight chance of survival while the other two drivers were given a sixty-five percent chance of survival, but they did not survive. As I massaged his body, most of his upper torso was covered in burn scars, except for where the seatbelt crisscrossed over his chest. He was also missing a few fingers, and his face and neck were scarred too. I was reluctant to ask questions about the crash, but I did.

"How did you possibly escape damage to your lungs

with the intense heat?" I asked during one of his massages. I knew he was a miracle to behold, and his positive energy was enlightening and energizing to me. He was lying on the massage table faceup at the time with his eyes closed.

He opened his eyes and looked up at me, right into my eyes, and raised his right hand pointing his index finger in the air. "That's why I survived!" he said directly at me. "I had my mouth covered with protective gear and didn't inhale the heat like the others did. I'm impressed that you ask that. Most people don't understand how the healing process takes oxygen, and that's what our lungs do."

"That only makes sense to me. I've not seen scars like this and with the obvious signs of your harness belt, the heat had to be intense," I said. "Thank you for telling me."

He was a motivational speaker and traveled a bit, and he also presented me with a book he coauthored. I still have it, and it inspires me when I see it on my bookshelf.

Dehydration Is Dangerous!

One hot summer morning, while setting up for massages in the poolside cabana, a couple came up to me inquiring about a massage, and we got them scheduled. Each had an hour massage, and I cautioned them during and after their massages that it was an extremely hot, summer day and that massages can dehydrate the body. Being in the sun will also dehydrate the body, and they were already drinking alcohol which is a dehydrator.

"All three of these dehydrators can have a profound effect on the body," I reiterated.

Two days later, this couple came to find me to tell me what happened to them after ignoring my warnings.

"Lynn, we didn't believe you when you said we needed to drink water after a massage. We went back to our lounge chairs and drank beer—a couple each or more. We fell asleep in the sun and don't remember anything until we woke the next morning in our camper. A couple of friends told us we were sleeping, and then drinking again, and talking out of our minds. After getting into the pool, they took us to our camper later that afternoon where we passed out until the next day. We don't remember anything after the massages. And we're so glad we were among friends. We will never do that again."

Special Requests

Then there was the fellow who came in requesting a deep tissue massage. As I started working on him—and I usually include stretches or some traction with the neck and shoulders, depending on the condition of patient/client—this guy said, in a casual but demanding voice, "Go ahead and adjust my neck. It is tight and needs one."

I calmly replied, "I don't do chiropractic adjustments if that's what you are asking of me."

A few minutes passed, and again he made a remark sounding somewhat irate.

"Oh, go ahead and do it! I know you know how."

"Sorry, man, I don't do chiropractic," I repeated again.

"Look!" he said. "I'll pay you an extra twenty dollars to give me an adjustment."

"Sorry, sir, I don't do adjustments. If you prefer, I can stop now so you can leave, and you won't owe me anything. My license is for massage therapy, not chiropractic."

"No, please continue," he said.

It wasn't until after he had paid and left that I wondered why he was so adamant about me giving him a neck adjustment. Then I thought he may have been testing me to see if I would take a bribe or insult to get me to do something other than massage. I take what I do seriously and won't jeopardize my license. Besides, I have not been trained in chiropractic neck adjustments and would be mortified if I were to injure someone. We have subtle ways of doing things. We also take an oath.

DO NO HARM.

Was he a cop? Maybe? I never saw him again.

Construction Worker

This man came in to have his arms and shoulders worked on, on Sundays—sporadically at first. Then he started coming in almost every Sunday, but he was getting worse instead of better. He said the massage kept him moving, but one day he came in, his whole arm was shaking from overwork. I asked about his workload, and he admitted that he worked every day, mostly twelve hours a day, and I could tell he was overworking.

"Tell me. Do you wield a hammer all day without a nail gun or anything?"

"Yes, that's right."

"You can't do that without any downtime," I said.

"I have to. I have to work," he said.

"I understand that, but your body is going to shut you down if you don't take time off, and you won't be able to work! Especially the labor-intensive work you do!"

I asked him to go see a chiropractor friend of mine for another assessment, and he refused. After a few weeks, I was so concerned that I refused to work on him unless he promised me he would go see this chiro.

"I will not touch you unless you promise me you will see this chiropractor."

He glared at me, and with his arm shaking, he said, "Okay! Will you please help me today?"

"Yes, of course. But I really want you to get a second opinion on your condition."

He came back the following week and thanked me for insisting he see him.

"What did he say?"

"Same thing you did. If I didn't take time off, my body was going to shut me down, and I'm on the verge of a collapse."

"Thank you. Thank you."

"Yes, and I am going to see him again," he said.

He continued to see me, and after being forewarned that his health was at risk, he began taking time off and continued getting better. Over the following weeks, I saw the chiropractor, Dr. T., and I asked his opinion about our mutual client, the construction worker.

"He was working himself into serious trouble." Dr. T then informed me—which I didn't know—that he was also able to help with the man's young son who had autism and special needs. The reason the single father was working so much was to provide for his autistic son. Dr. T. was able to help with him also, and they worked out an affordable plan while getting him the proper care that was needed. Ultimately taking the pressure off gave them a new lease on life.

Years later, our paths crossed. I recognized him vaguely but was unsure who he was until he said my name and then I recognized his voice. He thanked me again for what I had done for him.

"Thanks, but I was just at the right place at the right time. Glad I could be there!"

Out of the Norm!

During our stay in North Georgia, I acquired a regular

client who lived nearby. He was an elderly gentleman and he informed me that he was retired from a New York law firm and liked this area, so had settled here. Supposedly, he had been married a few times but was now living alone. He would come to the resort and lounge at the pool and read his books. About once a month, he would come in for a massage. I remember on one occasion, he came in for a massage two days in a row. When he came in the second day, I was a little surprised, and he told me the first one felt so good that he thought he would get another one. He seemed genuine, but I was a little suspicious. Whenever I felt a bit suspicious, I would introduce the client to my husband, Ernie. It was just a little introduction to let them know I wasn't available and my hubby was close by.

As it turned out this fellow—let's call him Norman—was a genuine gentleman, and we became very good friends.

He had a double hip replacement, a heart bypass, and a few other health issues in his life. He was very pleasant to be around and knowledgeable about finances which became helpful during the years we knew him.

One incident with him came late in the summer one year, when he had trouble with one of his hip replacements. He had to go get his replacement redone. I massaged him prior to going to the hospital, wished him luck, and said I would look forward to seeing him after the new replacement. And I would help him get well afterward.

About three weeks later, Norman rang my doorbell and was standing there with crutches, looking defeated and disheveled in the worst way, asking me for a massage, and could I please help him.

"Oh my goodness, Norm!" I said to him while opening the door. "You look awful. When did you get out of the hospital?"

"I checked myself out and came straight here," he said as he fumbled his way up the step through the doorway. "I'm not feeling too good. I just couldn't stay there anymore. I got a bone infection and have a shunt in my arm to give myself injections. They had to show me how, but I can do it."

"You drove by yourself here, from the hospital, in your condition? I tried to visit you while I was in Atlanta a week ago, but I got turned around and lost because of road construction," I told him as I assisted him into my massage room and on the table. He had an awful smell as I helped him take off some of his clothes.

"When was the last time you showered?" I asked.

"It's been too long because my incision needs to heal, and I'm not healing. Since I got that infection in the bone, I'm not healing. I'm sorry to ask, but can you bathe me too?"

Then I noticed his hip replacement incision. Numerous stitches were all red and inflamed. I threw a clean sheet over him to help keep his body heat in.

"Okay, you get off your feet and try to get comfortable as well as you can, and I'll be back in a few minutes."

I went into the kitchen and filled a large, stainless-steel, mixing bowl with hot water, and picked up a washcloth and soap from the bathroom. I brought it back to him to wash his face and arms and torso. The warm water felt good to him. He wiped the cloth over his head, not that there was much hair there. I could tell he was starting to feel better.

I dumped the bowl in the bathroom sink and refilled it again so I could wash his legs and feet. I carefully washed around the shunt in his arm and around the stitches on his thigh. He rolled from side to side so I could wash his back.

I gave him a towel and dumped the water again. When I came back this time, I brought a smaller bowl and a bottle of rubbing alcohol, and poured some in the bowl to dip my fingers in the alcohol so I could massage each of his sutures. I tried to use a cotton ball or swab, but it would stick to the stitches and didn't work to my satisfaction. So, dipping my fingers into the bowl, I massaged around each stitch as gently as I could as he fell asleep. That was usual for Norm. He usually fell asleep during his massages. But this was different, he was ill and exhausted this time.

He rested a little then wanted to get home to his own bed. So Ernie came in, and we helped him up to dress and out to his car, feeling renewed.

He came back a few days later, still on crutches, and I went over the stitches again and they were clean. There was no redness anywhere, and he was going back to the doctor to get stitches and the shunt removed. I didn't ask him for money, but he gave me two $100 bills, saying it was worth more and thanked me for helping.

It wasn't long after that he was back at the pool with his books and more massages.

We remained in touch for years until he passed away.

Chapter 9
Opening Doors

I often say that massage therapy opened doors for me that I didn't know existed. I liken it to walking through a hallway of doors. Open one, and I learned massage and anatomy. Onto the next, let's learn reflexology, then the next one, sport massage and repetitive-use injuries therapy. Next are Reiki, chakras, energy, and auras . . . What is next? Cranial sacral I, II, III, IV, and V . . . And next, cupping, hot stones, cold stones, aroma therapy, color therapy, flower therapy. The corridor can get longer as new modalities are brought forward, and the doors seem endless. Some are a little farfetched for me, so I leave those closed. But the hallway led me to Thailand to learn Thai massage. I'm still in that corridor of doors, looking for what is next. Part of the enjoyment of massage is to keep learning new techniques and meeting new people. It is hard work for the compensation.

As of the writing of this book, Ernie and I have been married fifty-one years, and I've been a massage therapist for twenty-two years.

* * *

My dad passed away May of 2000, the second year after we moved to Georgia. First Ernie's dad and then mine. Our moms were widowed after fifty-four years married.

We lived in Georgia three summers then decided to move to Florida. That state required a license. Now, three years after graduating from massage school, I needed to take a test to get a license to practice massage in Florida.

I went to a testing center in Atlanta to take the test. It was $250, and I sat for the test cold turkey and failed it by two points. What a disappointment. I expected the exam to cover massage and anatomy/physiology, but approximately one-fourth of the exam was about Eastern medicine—the one thing I had not taken any classes on. I didn't know about meridians and chakras. We didn't study any of that in school. I read a book about chakras once. It was a recommended read from the lady that gave me my first massage but was hard to understand. My interest wasn't there, but I needed to rethink it.

I went home, regrouped, and pulled out my medical anatomy book and went through the book page by page, and refreshed myself on anatomy and physiology. I picked up a book about Asian medicine to enlighten me on that and also a new book on contraindications for massage. After six weeks of an intensive, at-home refresher course, I felt ready to retake the test. Another $250, and the lady at the testing center said I passed with a high score, but when I asked what I got she said she wasn't allowed to tell me that.

"You told me how much I failed it by six weeks ago, but you can't tell me what I scored if I pass?"

"That's right," she said. "I can tell you that you scored really high on contraindications. Congratulations."

Now tell me. Does that seem fair? As I walked to my

car from the testing center, I looked at the papers she gave me and thought that was a lot of money and time for this. I hoped to make it pay off.

> *I have learned so much more of what massage is about by hands-on experiences than classes can teach. Some things science and chemistry can't explain.*
>
> *It's in God's Hands.*

Another motto of mine: "Education is expensive, no matter how you get it!"

Acutely honed skills come from the desire to learn and practice.

Massage therapy is a listening touch! Listen to what the client is saying with ears, and listen to what the body says by touch.

> *We did exercises in class where we stood facing each other with our hands up, touching fingertips together.*
>
> *Looking into the eyes of your classmate, hands touching, trying not to giggle at first, but then get serious. You closed your eyes and slowly withdraw the fingertips from the other person's hand without seeing them. One would move hands up, down, or side to side, and the other would feel for the movement with eyes closed and concentration. When you opened your eyes, you would see if you were close to the other person's hands.*
>
> *Another exercise, we place both hands on the person's back while they were lying face down. Then you slowly removed your hands without them knowing it.*

I did that in a class, and walked away to sit down, and it was three minutes before she realized I wasn't touching her!

Chapter 10
Moving to Florida!

We made the move to Florida. Now I was lost, for I didn't know where to go to apply for my license. I passed the licensing test before we left Georgia but that didn't get me a license. Now what?

During that unsettling time, I had taken an odd job or two—even house sitting—as I put massage away for a few months. I answered an ad from the newspaper for a job and found myself working for a telemarketing service selling vacation cruises. Let me tell you, that was an experience. I had no clue how that worked, but it was easy to learn, as I was told I became good at it. At least, they said I was. I got the hang of it quick and made some money, but the kids doing this stuff loved it and the opportunities it provided to travel. I gave them my two weeks and said no thank you. They asked me to stay because I had a good voice for it, meaning I sounded honest and sincere. But it made me feel shady. It was all legitimate, as those ships needed to get filled, it just wasn't for me. Thanks, but no thank you.

It was time to get back to what I really loved, trained, and paid for.

After asking questions, I had to apply for the Florida

license by going to a local massage school in Florida where, for a small fee, a lady there went online to get my transcripts transferred from Ohio and helped get the paperwork submitted. Six weeks later, I received my license through the mail. Now I was ready to get back to massaging.

Almost Always

I begin a massage with my client faceup. I explain that I prefer to begin faceup, and nine out of ten times when I leave the room for them to undress and get all set with clean sheets to slip between, they will be facedown. Most will be facedown to protect their vulnerabilities.

Most advertisements present a person facedown for the all-important back rub.

It is instinctive to want to protect our vulnerable front. Our skin is thinner in the front and gets thicker as it goes to our back. If something comes at you, we instinctively turn our backs to the projectile to protect our front. Instinct is good.

When I have a new client, I want to make eye contact, communicate and make a connection with them by starting with the hands, like a universal handshake. I prefer to massage hands first and work up both arms, communicating with them with firm or light pressure to build trust and feeling what their tolerances are for firmness, letting them have control of their massage.

> *When the frail eighty-three-year-old lady tells me she wants deep tissue, it's a lot different than the thirty-something-year-old, muscle-bound, athlete asking for the same thing. I need to know what their tolerances are, and I can do that analysis without causing harm by massaging hands and arms first.*

Then the neck and shoulders. By the time we get to the backside, we've built a trust and the client usually melts on the table.

While I am massaging a client and realize something is noticeably wrong, it is easy to tell that the person can't let their mind or body relax. Or the first-time client who is nervous about being massaged by someone they don't know. That's when I ask the question "Do you want to talk about it?"

I can usually tell by the tension of the body if it is work related or family related. Or if there is trauma after some sort of incident or accident. If the answer is no, we can either be silent or quietly talk. Mostly, they don't want to talk at first, and sometimes it makes things worse for them, which makes it harder for them to relax.

Depending on what is bothering them, it will trigger a past-experience or memory in my head. As I massage them, I will chat with them about their condition or pain, ask how their work and family lives are, get those thoughts out of the way. Those things may be the need for escape. If all else fails to alleviate the tension they're holding onto, I may tell a story. Something to help take their mind off their pain or troubles. Even adults like to hear a story.

It helps to talk or vent about them or their family or job; I become a listener, bringing up pleasant times that got them to where they are today, ask about the names of their kids, and how they met their spouse. Plus, as I work on a person, I listen with my ears as well as my hands. I pride myself on being able to get people to relax, giving them warmth and comfort like a mother figure who loves unconditionally and is without judgment. My voice is soft and low as I speak and I've been told the sound of my voice helps them to relax. As they melt onto the massage table, I can feel the tensions ease, making my work less strenuous. Telling a story humanizes me. Once we break that barrier, and confirm that I'm not a robot and I am human and not intending any harm or judgment whatsoever, they start to feel like someone cares.

Occasionally, something can trigger a bad memory that can put them back on edge. It can be perfume, or music, or a slight touch that triggers a panic response.

I don't wear perfume while I work anymore but lots of different fragrances and essential oils are available for whatever suits a particular mood. And I have different music to play for different people. I have a lady that can't stand piano music and another fellow who loves to hear only that. Some clients, who are also musicians, only want to hear white noise.

> One woman used to insist on a six a.m., Saturday morning (she wanted to come at five a.m., but I drew the line at six) for a two-hour massage once a month to a CD of singing bowls. I would set the player for repeat as the CD was only thirty minutes! I would get up at five to be awake and fresh at six, and listen to singing bowls for two hours, repeating every thirty minutes, while doing her body work, and she preferred silence after the first thirty minutes. I would later crawl back into bed after she left. If you have trouble sleeping . . . turn on the sound of singing bowls. Zzz.

A Triggered Flashback Reaction

I brushed against a woman's throat with my hand as I was massaging her neck. She was faceup with her eyes closed, and my hand came up under her neck and across her shoulders, then across the chest at the collar bone then back to her neck and brushed her throat. She opened her eyes and froze with panic, then asked what I was doing. I apologized right away, for I knew what had caused her to panic. I put both of my hands on her shoulders and patted lightly, trying to dissipate her panic. I spoke to her in a whisper, saying she was safe and away from any harm.

Her ex-husband used to cup his hand around her throat and push her up against the wall or lift her up the wall by her throat with her feet dangling.

She took a few deep breaths and calmed down. But the flashback was real.

Getting Grounded

Sometimes, there is a need to just get grounded in nature. If the person is highly stressed and there is a need to meld into something to change direction of the brain—so many people have trouble turning off their brain from responsibilities—I'll ask, "What is your favorite flower or color?" "Where is your favorite place in the world?" Usually, it is the beach, and I will ask them, "Let's take a walk on the beach. Tell me your favorite beach." And they do! "As we walk along the beach at water's edge, feel the water come up and wrap around your ankles. It's cold at first and then recedes, and the sand beneath your feet sinks and then your feet sink into the sand." A sunny warm walk on the beach.

This usually melts them into the table as I continue kneading their sore spots, or helps to drain away tensions.

A Story from My Childhood

I am in my late sixties now and sometimes surprise my-self with how much is stored in my brain. To be able to recall something that happened in my past amazes me. Things that are seemingly unimportant and tucked away, and yet, while working and chatting with a client, I'll be reminded of something that I once experienced. It helps to tell a story to ease the mind of the person on the table away from their own troubles. Sometimes it can be early years of my childhood that I am amazed I recall.

Here is a real story that actually happened in my life—a story like a book read to a child to listen and wonder about:

I was about eight years old when I had a wart on the end of my index finger. I think it was my right hand, but it was a wart that I would pick at and make bleed. It was during the summer, and we were vacationing in Kentucky where my dad was from. It was a long ride for us from Ohio since this was before the interstate was built.

We were in a small town near Somerset and Lake Cumberland. My dad's brother, Uncle Ray, lived on the side of a mountain where we were visiting. This was near the Appalachian Mountain area, and Uncle Ray didn't have running water. They had an outhouse, and Aunt Ruthie cooked on a woodburning cookstove. This was in the late fifties.

I was picking at my wart, and Dad told me to go out the back door and follow the foot path to the next house up the mountain to see my great Uncle Sy, and he would take care of that bothersome wart. I was frightened at first, but I was adventurous.

The path was well worn through a grassy meadow and easy to follow among the bushy trees. I was soon up the mountain to a wood cabin surrounded by a short—but not too short—unpainted, picket fence. I stood and looked over the gate. Within the fence were guineas, chickens, ducks, and various critters, which came running to me as I opened the gate with a squeak and stepped inside. I closed it right away so none of them would escape.

Uncle Sy was sitting on the front porch whittling, with the dog at his feet, and looked up at me after noticing the critters running at the gate squeaking. I stood for a moment as I was greeted by the welcoming committee of farm animals. Even the dog came up, wagging his tail with friendly licks. I was a farm girl and very familiar with all these kinds of animals, although I was fascinated with the guineas, my hands extended to them to pet and touch. I could make a pet out of anything back then and was not afraid of them. Guess I was an animal charmer, not like kids are today, afraid of everything.

Great Uncle Sy stood up from his chair, put his knife away by closing it against his leg, and slipped it in his overalls' bib pocket. He stepped down from the porch and told me to come on up so he could see me. I made my way through the reception of animals begging for my attention until I reached the steps of the porch where he stood. He looked down at me.

"You're Robert's girl, aren't you?"

"Yes." I nodded. And then he invited me to come up and sit on the porch as he called to Aunt Sybil through the old screen door of the cabin.

"We have a visitor."

Great Aunt Sybil brought us out a cold drink of water. She lingered and said hello, looked me up and down, and muttered how I had grown, then retreated back into the cabin. When he asked me why I had come up alone, it was as if he knew there was a reason.

"My daddy told me to come visit because you could take this wart off my finger." I held it up to show him, but after seeing him with his pocketknife, I wasn't quite so sure I wanted him to. But still, I wasn't frightened of him. He was old looking with wrinkly, dark, tanned, leathery skin. I sat down on the hanging porch swing and straightened my dress as he sat on his straight-back chair, and he looked at my finger. He asked me to stand up and I stood in front of him, then he took my hand and said, "This is not going to hurt. I'm going to charm it off for you."

He then proceeded to gently touch each of his ten fingertips in small circles on my wart while seemingly praying or whispering something undistinguishable.

"Now, don't pick at it anymore, forget about this and it will disappear in a couple of weeks. Understand?" he asked. "Is there anything else?"

Well, I was curious, and asked him if he could tell me how he predicts the weather, especially the winters. I had overheard adults talking once and heard that Uncle Sy knew all about weather predicting. There was a long pause as he stared at me, making me a little uneasy and then . . .

"Well, let me tell you one thing: count the fogs in August and that will tell you how many snows we're going to have. That's a start. I'll tell you more the next time."

After that, I walked back down the hill on the path from which I had come.

I don't remember ever seeing him again.

About two weeks later, after we got back home to Ohio, I was laying on our living room floor watching TV when I remembered to look at my finger, and the wart was completely gone. The charm worked!

This little true story usually gets people relaxed. As I tell the story, they can relate to it and let their minds drift to other places or can divert their attention away from their own troubles. So many of my clientele are business executives or highly stressed, working people, and these stories help distract them from business or family for just an hour. That gives their minds a break as well as the body.

Chapter 11
Tuning In or Tuning Up?

Bodyworker!

When a person, especially a first-time client, on my massage table tells me, "That didn't hurt until you started pressing on it," I tell them, "A massage will tune you into yourself. Not only a tune up but tune in too." Strange how a small spot or area on the body will have an "owie" here and there, unknown to the person before I started to work on them. It they want to know, I will explain that this little "owie" could be a blocked lymph node or a little, fatty tissue under the skin unknown to them. That's what I do. As I massage the surface of the skin and move my hands in the direction of the venous blood flow, it also moves with the lymph flow, like plumbing, which can also move any blockages of the lymphatic system. Massaging toward the heart improves lymphatic drainage and superficial blood flow back to the heart.

"The most healthy part of a massage." Getting tuned into their body while getting a tune up!

"You sure know a lot about the body," I often hear.

"Well, that's what I do. I studied the muscles and nerve innervations and keep learning with each client that comes to see me for whatever problem they may have. Massage isn't just to feel good but a health benefit," I say!

Massage Therapy to Bodywork

I consider myself a bodyworker as much as a massage therapist.

In December 2000, I decided to take a course in repetitive use injury therapy (RUIT).

This was a three-day seminar held in a hotel in Nashville, Tennessee. It was my first seminar since graduation. A year out of massage therapy school, and now back to school again, learning. "Education is expensive no matter how you get it."

The course, the hotel, and the drive to and from was nearly $1,000. This sounded very exciting, and it taught me some techniques of massage that helped advance not only my knowledge of massage but also allowed me to meet peers and help many of the clients who were coming to me for various types of massage. I had needed to broaden by skills.

Most people who need massages are not looking for relaxation but therapy. We need relief from injuries due to repetition. I help people by pointing out the reasons for their injuries as they tell me what they do on a daily basis. Whenever I meet someone for the first time, the first question I ask is what do they do, to find out whether it is work-related or sport.

We all get into routines and mold our bodies into that groove. It can be kneading bread, stirring a pot, lifting weights.

I met a woman who was a scrub nurse for twenty-two years. I once said to her as I was massaging her,

"You stand with your weight on your left foot, with your right foot turned slightly to the right to stand sideways against the operating table, handing instruments to the surgeon across the table."

"That is exactly right. How do you know that?"

"Because your body is molded that way!"

She was astounded at that tidbit of information.

Anyone sitting at a desk daily in front of computers are all too common nowadays. Stand-up desk? How I wished I had one back in the '90s. All athletes, marathon runners, body builders, gymnasts, mechanics, men who sit with a wallet in their pocket and wonder why their back hurts on one side, ladies carrying a heavy purse on one shoulder, brief cases, and telephones, the list goes on and on.

When I was a stay-at-home mom with an infant and a toddler, I joined a bowling league. We would bowl each Tuesday afternoon during naptime for the kids. A time for moms to get out with kids and be with other moms.

I worked up to throwing a fourteen-pound ball. My pals said the heavier the better to improve my game. I watched some of those women throw a sixteen-pounder, and I just couldn't do it. A fourteen-pound ball was too heavy for me. I tried but I should have listened to my body and bowled with a lighter ball.

Every week, I was at the chiro because I was throwing my back out. He said I either needed to give it up or start throwing the ball on the left side and the right side to keep me balanced. (joking, of course). Plus, when I had to carry a diaper bag, two kids, and a purse, that also added to the unbalance of things.

During that time in my life, I saw the chiro so much for back problems. Wish I'd known about massage then.

I often see young moms and grandmothers who carry kids on the hip and they wonder why their backs and knees hurt!

The world is constantly changing, and we must change with it.

Almost everything we do today has some kind of repetitive motion to it.

This class was beneficial for me and my massage practice. So much so that I decided to attend the class again two years later and got so much more from it the second time. It was the same instructor, but in a different city.

The second time I took this class, it was in North Atlanta. Only this time, I lived in Florida. I planned the trip to drive from Florida to Ohio for a visit with my mother. Then back to North Atlanta for the three-day seminar, then to Florida after. That's a long drive alone.

I met a lady, Judy, and we teamed up for the session. We were close to the same age, married the same number of years with kids, We were older than most of the people in the class. She was from the Atlanta area. We became life friends during that seminar. During that class, the instructor was giving a demonstration, on the calf, and how to work the gastrocnemius and IT band on the lower lateral leg, when he spun around looking for someone out of a room of fifty-plus people.

ME! Pointing his finger at me, he said, "You're gonna love this one!"

Judy and I looked at each other with questioning look.

"What did he mean by that?" I asked her.

"Maybe he sees something we don't," she replied.

We decided she would be on the table first for me to get the feel of this new technique he was demonstrating. When we attend these seminars, it is customary to wear some sort of sport attire. Most of us wear sports bras and T-shirts with spandex, yoga pants, or shorts so we can get on and off the massage table quickly and easily.

Judy was wearing shorts and was easily workable. Before she got on the table, we talked about yoga and how she had multiple surgeries, including a mastectomy from breast cancer and reconstruction. She took yoga classes too and could stand up straight and bend over to touch her forehead to her knees. My jaw dropped, and this gal was not a thin woman. I was envious of her flexibility. She got on the table, and I practiced the new technique on her.

When it came my turn to get on the table, I pulled my yoga pants up to above my knees so my calves were bare for her to feel the muscles. The movement we were learning was for the client to lay facedown with knees bent so their calves and feet were in the air. Judy took hold of my calf and slid her thumb, with a little pressure, from the ankle bone on the lateral side of leg to the knee, and I let out a scream. I was embarrassed about being so loud as to draw attention to myself. It felt like she cut me with a hot knife. It burned, and I raised my head and looked around at my leg. I just knew I felt blood running down my leg.

"What did you cut me with?" I said accusingly and with tears in my eyes.

"I don't have anything in my hands!" she said, holding her hands out. I laid my head down and cried for a minute until the pain subsided, and then apologized to her for accusing her.

"Try it again, please," I asked her. "But gently, please."

She massaged my leg again, and I could feel how tight my legs were. It was good practice for her, as she could feel the tightness. That is how we learn how to differentiate these things. The gentler massage was needed for me, and she worked my legs to soothe the tension. We both agreed I had been under too much stress from all the driving I had done in a short time. I still had the long drive home to Tampa after the seminar. But being in a massage class helped improve circulation and sleep.

I learned a lot from the first session two years before, but you get information overload sometimes in these classes, and I took much more away from this one. I had shared that with Judy during our time together, and she also took the class again a couple of years later and was glad she did.

During these classes, you can usually find someone to massage or trade a massage with. It's cool when someone has a technique to share. Learning from each other is a bonus.

Like I said, this was my second time attending this seminar two years apart, and it was worth the time and money.

Chapter 12
Adding to
My Business Card

Reflexology

I revved up by taking a different class. I finally discovered the person I wanted to learn reflexology from— a Native American woman who only did reflexology and had done so for thirty years. I called immediately, and she asked me a few questions and said she still had an opening. She only taught six people at any one time, so I sent in my tuition to guarantee a spot. She sent me a packet via mail, that included instructions and diagrams of detailed pressure points on the feet, what to wear (white or light-colored clothing), and a recipe of herbs and spices for a detox bath between classes.

Reflexology . . . YES!

What an exciting modality to me!

If anyone had told me at a young age that I would enjoy massaging other people's feet, I would have told them they were crazy.

But here I am, fascinated with the foundation on which we walk: our feet!

After receiving the packet, I was excited. It sounded like an adventure, and I was very curious as I looked over the paperwork she provided.

The class was in Atlanta near an industrial area, and I had my hotel room reserved close by and drove up from Tampa the day before. As I drove, a tooth started to ache about halfway through the drive and developed into an abscessed tooth. The pain was nearly debilitating. I found my hotel to be very nice and got checked in.

Thankfully, I was able to call my dentist and let them know my situation to get a prescription called in; but I couldn't pick it up until later the next day. Strict rules applied with these classes. If you are late or miss time in a class, you don't get credit for the class, and class started early, before I could get to or find the drug store.

The instructor was clear.

"Did everyone get the packet I sent?" Everyone nodded. "Everyone should wear white or light colors, and all metal are to be removed. Rings, earrings, any metal." Someone asked if that included belt buckles.

"It's metal, isn't it? Metals and dark colors block energy. To get the most out of this class, we must be able to focus and let energy flow. Especially with reflexology." Everyone took off jewelry and belts with buckles and put them away.

"During and after class, you are to eat light, and at the end of the day, you need to take a detox bath. Is that clear?"

"Yes!" Everyone said.

As introductions were made at the beginning of class, I painfully confessed my tooth situation, as I had to keep ice in my mouth to ease the pain. When the instructor asked if anyone in the class had any colloidal silver, one woman spoke up and said, "Never leave home without it." She rummaged through her purse.

I had never heard of it before and didn't know what to do with it. Someone came up with a first-aid kit and retrieved a couple of cotton swabs. They took the cotton out and told me to wet the cotton with colloidal silver and put it on the tooth. Pain gone, just like that.

That was amazing. The pain would come back in about an hour, and I would rewet the cotton and the pain would go away. We only had thirty minutes for lunch, and I asked the ladies where the nearest store was so I could get some of that silver stuff. It took me twenty minutes to get there and back, thankfully, but there wasn't enough time for lunch.

I managed to get through that first day and get my prescription started that night, took that detox bath, and slept long and hard, even on a strange bed.

It's absolutely mystifying and miraculous what foot massage can do for the body. The connection between our feet and the rest of the body is a treasure we take for granted.

By the third day, as we gathered around the water cooler waiting for class, we all six of us had a noticeable glow about us. One of the other students mentioned how, after two days of reflexology and detox baths, she had a bowel movement that felt like a colon cleanse. We all laughed and agreed with her. Hence our glow. My abscessed tooth was feeling better. I already had an appointment to address that when I got back home.

Ever since I had taken up massage, I knew there was something special about our feet, but I couldn't understand it. That's why I wanted to learn details of what it was all about.

About six months after the class, I was traveling through Atlanta and called ahead to let our instructor know I wanted to meet with her if she had any time available. She invited me to her studio to view her paintings and sit in her beautiful teepee and we meditated. As I drove away that afternoon, I thought to myself, *I knew this was going to be an adventure.*

Reflexology was added to my business cards.

Active Isolated Stretching

Ernie and I talked about moving back to Georgia. I was traveling back and forth to Ohio to visit my mom in assisted living.

Time was coming up for me to renew my license, and I never liked taking a class just to get CEUs—Continuing Education Credits. I wanted to learn something I was interested in. One of my idol therapists was a man by the name of Aaron L. Mattes. He presented us with AIS—Active Isolated Stretching.

AIS is similar to repetitive therapy but more in the order of sports massage. My license renewal was due later in the year, but I didn't like waiting until the last minute. I heard of this class, in the fall of 2005, and signed up right away.

So, I was off to Atlanta again in March 2006 for a class with an admired therapist, who was also from Florida. I also made this trip with intentions of contacting a realtor for a quick look at properties in North Georgia. I wanted to get back to North Georgia where it was cooler in the summer.

Our current plan was to have our place in Florida for winter and do summer in Georgia, like a snowbird. Plus, I would have a place to stay on my trips back and forth to Ohio. That's one thing about working as a massage therapist: I have flexibility for work and travel.

The AIS class was held at a hotel near the Atlanta airport. I was the first at class each morning at eight a.m. Mr. Mattis was usually already there working on someone. People would employ his time before and after class, and he would accommodate them. I enjoyed watching him work. I felt like a teenager watching a rock star. And what luck; there were only about thirty-five people in this class, and he said he didn't usually teach a class of less than fifty.

Since some of us had signed up so early, he didn't want to disappoint. There would have been more in attendance, but a chiropractor school was taking finals that week, plus it was St. Patrick's weekend. Most of the people in this class were chiropractors, with only about nine massage therapists, one MD, and six of his assistants. We got our money's worth, as we were well supervised while learning new techniques to help others.

After the class was over late Sunday afternoon, I drove home from South Atlanta to Tampa, armed with more knowledge that would benefit my athletic clients. Now I can add "Sports Massage" to my business cards.

Chapter 13
Shady Places?

I worked for a brief period at a Japanese massage establishment in Tampa, and I do mean brief.

The outside advertised Japanese massage and spa with photos of Geisha ladies. When I went in to ask if they needed any therapists, I knew I was in the wrong place for me. I wasn't even sure they would want me as I'm not Asian nor do I look like anything like it. I'm five-foot-eight and a bit taller than most Asian people. But I was curious about how they ran things there.

As I stepped inside the door of a very small waiting area, a twenty-something Asian man greeted me through a darkened slide window so as not to see in. He was pleasant enough and gave me a tour of the establishment. He was the only person in there and I felt a bit uncomfortable. They had about five rooms all with massage tables with bars on the ceiling. There were small changing rooms for people to change in and lock their clothes then grab a towel to wrap around them for the steam room before going to a room for massage. Also, a breakroom for the therapists and a laundry room.

The young man was glad to have me work, and I asked about the others that worked there but there weren't any others at that time, he said. They all had to go back for the time being. He was very vague, and I knew something wasn't right, and I asked why he would even consider me. He said he needed someone right away who could help until the crew got back.

He himself was a massage therapist and would also massage the men that came in. I didn't see any women come in. He said if anyone gave me any "trouble," he would be close and just to let him know. I only had one man tell me after his massage that I had forgotten one muscle. And I politely told him he could handle that one himself as I slipped out the door.

The place reminded me of the movies when they guys would wrap a towel around them and sit in the steam room. Some did, some I'm not so sure.

During that first week, I informed the young man that this wasn't the place for me, and he asked me to stay to finish out the week and I did.

I was really glad to be out of there.

Not So Shady, BUT?

Now, where do I go from here? My girlfriend called me to tell me her chiropractor was looking for a massage therapist to work in his office. That was music to my ears, as I thought from day one that would be my dream job—a massage therapist working with a chiropractor to help people.

I called right away and set up an appointment. I met with Dr. C. and his wife, since she managed the office and scheduling. He had his office and two treatment rooms where he did adjustments, a separate therapy room with tables to lie on for electrical stimulations of muscles, a larger room with exercise equipment—such as bicycles, an inversion table, weights, and stretch devices—and a closet for doing massages. The room was hardly large enough for the table let alone a therapist. But it was a start. I accepted the position after percentage negotiations, and started that week for three days a week. We made a deal that I would also help out in the therapy room, helping people when I wasn't busy doing massages.

The office was open three or four days a week with one being a half day. Mrs. C. scheduled several massages a day for me, and it was great being a part of the office. Dr. C. was easygoing; he would often give me instruction about a client. I thought things were going smoothly until Mrs. C. raised her voice at me in a waiting room full of clients, demanding to know where I had been. I was taken aback by her sudden anger. I had been helping with clients earlier, but when duty calls to work on a client, that is my first priority.

"What are you talking about?" I was mystified that she didn't know. "I've been massaging a client that you scheduled for me an hour ago. I just finished and here I am!"

She was obviously agitated about something. "Well, I need you out here on the floor helping with clients in the therapy room."

"I'm here now and glad to help out when not massaging. Do I have anyone else on my schedule? I can't be in two places at once." I tried to ease her tension because I thought it was amusing, but she was stressed with clients and trying to find a blame for her error in judgment, and I was it.

Many Clues This Would Probably Be Short Term

The closet-converted-massage room I worked in was too small. I managed to set a CD player for music and a clock in a corner on the floor. As I worked around the table, my butt would be against the wall. I'm tall and not what you call thin.

One patient I worked on in that office was a real, big, muscular man, with shoulders so wide his arms wouldn't fit on the table. I did the best I could, massaging him with his feet hanging off the end and shoulders hanging off the edge, and when he turned over, I had to press up against the wall. He was covered with tattoos. Across the top of his back was a large tattoo of King Kong's head and shoulders with tree leaves dividing his tattoo from the rest of his back covered with more body art. That was entertaining. I guess I can say I massaged King Kong! I won't add that to my business card, but it does make an interesting story.

Mrs. C. also had an assistant working in the office, and she informed me that Mrs. C had a best friend who was also going to school for massage therapy and would be coming on board in the office when she received her massage license. I met the woman once and got the feeling she didn't have the desire to be a therapist at all, and she was about twice my size and that amused me as I took a mental picture of her in that little room with the table and a client.

I stuck it out for a couple of months until Dr. C. wanted to talk. I, too, was ready to talk to him, and we agreed I was not a permanent fit for his office. He felt I asked for too much money for a massage and should only get $15 per massage for my service, even though I supplied my own linens and lotions and worked the floor. We had agreed on an amount before I started working there, but Mrs. C. said I wasn't worth that; besides, I couldn't be in two places at once.

I left that day with renewed spirits and never returned.

Florida just wasn't shaping up for me as I had hoped.

Chapter 14
Unexplainable Incidents

Extra Company?

Many things come up along this journey as a massage therapist. One afternoon, in a small office, I recalled an incident when a mature gentleman of fifty or so came to see me for stress relief after visiting his father at a hospice care facility. His father, as I recall him telling me, was mostly in a comatose state, and we never know how much longer it will be when someone is in hospice care.

He undressed and was lying on the table covered with a sheet, and I worked on him systematically for about a half hour before I asked him to turn facedown on the table.

Suddenly, there was a strong, overwhelming sensation of someone else in the room. I kept looking over my shoulder and around the small room. I wasn't frightened, as it didn't feel evil but almost like the oxygen in the room became heavy. I had a strong feeling that it might have been the client's father, and perhaps he had died was what I thought. After about ten minutes without saying anything, as I massaged his back and legs, making my way around the table, the feeling left as quickly as it came, and

I saw a flash of light near the door. I stood straight up from working on his back and knew it was gone.

I only then asked my client, "Did you feel that?" I knew he wasn't asleep at the time like he usually was when I massaged his back.

"I sure did!" he said with enthusiasm.

"A sense of anyone you might know?"

He wasn't sure, and we didn't talk about it anymore. He did return again the following week, and his dad was still in the hospice facility. About a week later, his father did finally pass away. He came for one more massage after the funeral, and I didn't see him anymore.

Three Feathers

We were living in a condo near Tampa. My mother was now in assisted living, having a hard time coping. I would often make trips to Ohio to visit her, clean the house, and take care of things. A thousand-mile drive every six to eight weeks.

A morning prior to one of those drives north, I was waking from a dream of white clouds and could see three feathers from a white dove's wing fall from the clouds one at a time. I knew they were wing feathers because of the way they twirled point down.

They fell onto my stomach, one at a time, and I felt each one touch with a prick, and I jolted up out of my sleep. Ernie was next to me, and it startled him when I raised up with a jolt, the morning sun shining through the east window of our bedroom. I was looking around, searching for the feathers, and he asked me what I was looking for.

"Feathers! I saw three white feathers drop from the sky and felt them prick me on my belly!" I looked up at the twelve-foot-high ceiling, realizing what I had just said.

"Okay?" he said with bewilderment.

"The dream was real. I saw them and felt them prick me." I realized I was dreaming but it was so real, and I wondered what the significance of this meant. I knew it had to have something to do with the upcoming trip to Ohio. Mom hadn't coped well since Dad passed. It had something to do with her or him. I knew I would find out in Ohio. And I did.

I left the next day and drove seventeen hours to Mom's house. While there, I was working in the house to help clean out her office and such.

I was talking with Ernie on the cell phone late one evening at dusk. The reception was bad, and I stepped outside for a stronger signal. While standing on the sidewalk next to the house, I looked up and saw a large white dove sitting just above the door awning. He was merely ten feet from me, sitting there staring at me, and he was the largest dove I'd ever seen. I knew immediately who it was representing. I told Ernie about the bird, and then we said good-night and hung up. It was getting darker, and I took a few steps to the corner of the house and around to the front, and there I looked down and picked up a large, white, wing feather.

"That's one!" I said to myself, walking back to the side where I saw the dove. He was still there, watching me.

"A present for me? When and where will I find the others?" I asked as if he would answer me. "Thank you for coming to see me," I said to him as a tear slipped out the corner of my eye. I stood there, tears flowing, as I was happy and sad at the same time. I cry now as I write this memory. I was blessed at that moment!

I walked to my brother's house next door where I had left my car parked and spent the night at his house. The next morning, when I got up and stepped into the kitchen for coffee, my sister-in-law confronted me.

"You'll never guess what I saw sitting on top of your car this morning."

"A big, white dove, maybe?" I said, questioning.

"How did you know? I've never seen that bird around before, and he's a big one. Sitting right on the top of the rail on your car, above the driver door."

"Yes, he surprised me last night. Hope he's not pooping on my car though." I looked out the window and saw him there. "He's here visiting. I don't see any mess on the side, but it will wash off if he does. He's a good sized bird, all right, very distinctive."

An hour later, after breakfast and dressing, I walked back to the old house, and the big dove was walking in the driveway and other birds had gathered around him. He let me get close—about three feet from him—and I tried to entice him to come to me on my arm, but he wouldn't. I watched him fly up on the rooftop of the house. Another feather was found on the sidewalk near the door that afternoon.

The next day, in the late afternoon, I took a walk along the main road to clear my head and make a phone call. I walked about fifty yards and turned to look at the property. Everything was pretty and green, and it was a warm day near Sidney, Ohio.

I saw that dove flying in a big circle like he was flying the perimeter of the ten acres my parents owned. He flew around twice, flapping his wings and gliding in a big circle, and then made a third circle around the whole property. I was nearly standing on the road when I heard a car coming toward me, so I looked down to make sure I was safely out of the way. But still I wanted to watch this bird. It was so majestic, as this distinctive, white bird flew these circles. When I looked back again to see where he was, he had disappeared. I looked up and down and all around, but he was nowhere to be seen.

I never saw him again.

Two days later, when I was leaving to go back home, I found the third feather next to my car, and I smiled.

Chapter 15
Entities

An entity, or "spirit," is a controversial subject that happens occasionally. It often leaves me wondering, "What just happened?"

Some are friendly, and some are not. Most people are not open or tuned into these things.

It has been suggested I keep sage on my desk, wheatgrass over my door, and selenite crystals under my massage table to ward off any undesirable entities or spirits attached to people. I wear a watermelon tourmaline crystal on a neck chain and occasionally a hematite ankle bracelet on my right ankle when I suspect something out of the ordinary or get a new client.

When entities come with, or attach themselves to people, it can have some challenges with it.

One such happening, while working at a chiropractor's office, was a lady. I left the room for her to undress and get on the table. When I returned and started working on her hands and arms, as I do with a new client, I heard a giggle that came from outside the door. I thought nothing of it, but then I felt as if someone was in the room or outside the door in the hall. I excused myself to open the door and looked out, expecting someone to be there. Then I looked under the table and found nothing. Someone was there, and she was young.

Now, remember this was a first-time client, and I don't always let on when this type of strange thing happens. At one moment, I thought I saw a movement out the corner of my eye. And this was one of those times I blurted it out.

"Do you have a little girl with you?"

The lady looked up at me from the table, startled, and asked, "What do you mean?"

I was blunt and serious. "An attachment of sorts, a little guardian angel that you are aware of?" I didn't mean to sound like a nutcase. But then how do I not?

Then she admitted, "Oh, yes. I have this little, mischievous girl that likes to peak around corners. I'm very surprised you saw her!"

"Well, she is here," I said. "I think I let her in," shifting to humor. Once I discovered the little girl spirit, she got quiet.

"She does seem impish," I said. "She likes to play little tricks on people." The lady agreed that to be the case but was also amazed that I even noticed.

"She must like you," she said.

I inquired if she knew anything about her, which she didn't but said she can get quite mischievous sometimes and was used to having her around. The conversation was very casual, calm, and matter-of-fact.

The next time she came in, I didn't say anything about her companion, but I guess the little angel spirit thought I was no fun, and I didn't have an opportunity to feel or sense her presence again.

Problem Solved!

Rana, a regular client, had a son who was eight, and one day she called me to ask if I could see him.

"He asked to see you," she said. He came with her often when I worked on her, usually after school. He played games on his device while I worked on her. But this time, he was having a tightness in his lower back on his right side, and requested to see me. A little unusual but it happens.

She brought him in and helped him up on the massage table, lifted his shirt off over his head, and we both saw an unusual lump, the size of a small egg on the lower right quadrant of his back, just above the hip. We both saw it, spoke of it, and wondered what it was.

"Something new?" I asked. Neither of them knew about it.

I had him lie faceup, covered with a sheet. He was so small. I systematically worked his neck and shoulders while she sat in the chair next to the table. I asked him questions about the tightness he felt in his back, right where the lump was.

He said the pain came on suddenly and was with him all day after he had gotten to school that morning. I asked him to turn over, and I massaged up and down his small back to his hips. He said it felt better. As I massaged over the lump, it moved. Then I stretched him several ways across his back and had him turn over again to face up.

When I asked how he felt, he said he felt better and the pain was gone. Then asking him to sit up on the side of the table, I, too, noticed the lump was gone. We both looked for it. I then left the room to wash my hands and let her help pull his shirt back on over his head. He was so cute as he thanked me for helping, and he felt much better. She used the bathroom while I went in to change the sheets.

I pulled back the top sheet, noticing a lump on the bottom sheet identical to the lump on his back. My bottom sheets are fitted and smooth on the table, yet there was a lump in the sheet. I was afraid to touch it then, so I rolled up both sheets together in a ball and dropped them on the floor in the corner. I don't usually do that, but I wanted to keep those sheets separate from all the others. I quickly smoothed out the table pad to make sure it was okay. Then I put another set of clean sheets on the table, as I had another client coming in.

I didn't want to alarm anyone by announcing that he had an attachment to him. As they were leaving, they passed my next client coming in, and she stepped into the room as I closed the door behind them going out. She looked at me with wide eyes and shuttered like a chill.

"Okay," I said, "you felt something!"

"Yes, that was weird. That little boy had something attached to him, but it's okay now," she said. "Kids can pick up things at school sometimes. But that felt weird."

I told her he was the reason they were here, for me to look at him.

As we walked into the massage room, she felt it again. She looked directly at the sheets on the floor in the corner and said, "There it is in those sheets on the floor. Just keep them rolled up and put them in the wash, and let it go down the drain!"

"Yes, ma'am, that was my intention. Thank you for verifying it for me."

Problem solved!

Outside Massage

A special request from a client was for our first meeting to be an outside massage. It was a private setting, as I set up the table in the dewy, soft grass near palm and live oak trees of a Florida residence. A nice warm day was developing that morning with little to no breeze.

"The perfect setting," she said.

I was barefoot in the grass during the massage. It was early in my practice as a massage therapist, right after we had moved to Florida. As I walked around the table, working on her, I asked if she needed anything specific or if she had any pain areas that needed extra attention. Some crazy thing came over me as the atmosphere was magical.

"I've only been doing massage for about three years and have a lot to learn, and sometimes I feel as though someone guides my hands when I'm not always sure what to do."

Then I apologized to her for talking too much as I continued in silence.

When I finished, she sat up on the side of the table with the sheet wrapped around her and promptly explained to me I have a spirit guide with me all the time.

"This guide of yours is an ancient Spanish nun in full habit named Maria. You are right. She does keep watch over you and helps guide your hands when needed. You're lucky and blessed to have her. I enjoyed your massage, and you will be very good as you become more experienced."

I stood there with my jaw dropped open as she spoke to me. I thanked her for telling me and didn't know what else to say.

I never saw her again.

Thank you, Maria, for helping guide me during those years!

Little Feather

Before we moved to Georgia and purchased a house, I made sure it was clean of any such undesirable spirits. Our half-acre lot in a subdivision was on the side of a mountain slope and had a wooded area in the back—serene.

After we moved and settled in, my husband started landscaping the slope in the backyard, leveling places for stone walls, walks, steps, and bricks. We are outdoor people, and Ernie liked landscaping the backyard. The fruit trees, berry bushes, vegetables, and herbs were my thing. And the birds and bird feeders were his. And we both liked water features in the yard to have the sound of running water.

Every day during spring and summer, we were outside, and we noticed each day we found little feathers stuck in strange places. Sometimes I would find a little feather dangling from a web—and I mean a little feather; they were no longer than an inch. Sometimes they were a little bigger but not by much. And I started collecting the little feathers in a small vase-like jar. We didn't have to look for them; they were noticeable and would show up each morning. They were a variety of little bird feathers, with different patterns and colors from the little birds in our area.

Our kids and grandkids were coming to visit, and Ernie built a tree house out in the woods. It was our quiet space in the trees. He had cleared off space for a small trail. We had a variety of trees in the woods, so Ernie selected a pine tree in which to build a platform with a drop door in the bottom.

So, he made a ladder to climb up the trunk of the tree and push up the trapdoor on the bottom of the platform. It turned out more like a tree stand than a tree house, but it was about ten feet up and had a guard rail around it with a bench. The bench around the platform could seat about six, and the three grandkids could climb into it for a picnic.

Right after Ernie finished it, he asked me to come up and check it out. It was not really my thing, but I managed to climb up the ten-foot ladder, squeeze through the trapdoor, and let the door down, and sat for a while. It was nice. It smelled of the woods and had a beautiful vantage point that looked out over the roof tops to the mountains in the distance. Then I started noticing that I did not feel alone.

Ernie had walked away down below as I walked around the small platform and sat back down, thinking it a nice place to have a sandwich and a drink. Again, I looked around thinking someone was with me but only felt a light, warm, summer, Georgia breeze. Ernie came up then, and we discussed a few things about the platform and how the grandkids would like this. They were still very young—two, four, and six—and this would keep them entertained a while when they visited us from England. Then we got up, and opened the trapdoor, and climbed back down the ladder.

Later that afternoon when we came in for dinner, and we were calling it a day, we talked about the tree house, and I asked Ernie if he noticed any visitors in the woods.

"Do we have a spirit out in the woods?" I asked. "I didn't feel threatened by it, as it was friendly. This whole area around here was once Native American territory and reservation. Most of the spirits are Cherokee, being so close to the Trail of Tears."

"It seems so," he said. "I've noticed a few times while out there in the woods, and it stays in the woods and seems to really like the tree house since I built it."

It was a short time later when we had a friend over that knew of those things and confirmed our spirit friend was a young Native American maiden, and her name was Little Feather.

"That's why we find all the prominent little feathers each morning!"

Little Feather stayed around for a few years, and she would show us little feathers occasionally and make us smile, and that's how we knew it would be a good day. Then one day, I was out there in the woods sitting on a bench, and I felt melancholy and sadness coming from Little Feather. It was a sad-to-tears kind of feeling. I prayed for her so she could move on to be happy and told her we would miss her and cried for her. We don't see little feathers as often as we did during those years, but when we do see one, we think of her and smile.

Chapter 16
People See Me for a Variety of Reasons

Dress for Success

I was working at a private office with another massage therapist, near Tampa, located in a small plaza with about five other retail businesses. We were at a busy intersection with lots of exposure.

It was a small office with a reception room, two massage treatment rooms with a storage room for sheets and lotions, and a bathroom. We preferred appointments, but occasionally we would take walk-ins.

I was there just watching traffic when a fellow pulled up on his motorcycle, parked the bike on the kickstand, and stood up with a little crook in his back, unable to stand straight, then he headed to our door. He wore jeans and a short-sleeve shirt. He stepped inside and saw me sitting at the small desk.

He looked me up and down, saw I was wearing a scrub top, then, in a questioning voice, said, "Looks like I can get legitimate massage here?"

Anger bubbled up in me as I stood up and responded,

almost like a low growl, "Yes, and if you're looking for anything else, you've come to the wrong place."

He held out his arm, holding his hand up like he thought I was going to hit him. "No, ma'am. I just left one of those places." And then placed his hand on his back in pain. "I need a legitimate massage, please, my back hurts."

"Certainly, you came to the right place," I said, trying to smile.

You see, just the day before, I was patiently waiting for a client who was a few minutes late when a really hot-looking gentleman, with groomed hair and beard and a three-piece suit, came in, asking for a quick, ten-minute massage.

"Ten minutes?" I asked, questioning his request. "We usually do thirty minutes to ninety minutes—even two hours. I've never been asked for a ten-minute massage. Besides, I'm waiting on a client right now who is ten minutes late. If he doesn't show up in five minutes, I can work you in for thirty minutes?"

"Nah. Look, I'm just in need of a ten-minute quickie."

The hot-looking appeal shattered like glass and tumbled on the floor as I understood what he was asking, and I had to keep cool as I slowly stood up. Respectfully, I showed him our licenses framed on the wall, told him we were legitimate, licensed, massage therapists here, and that he had come to the wrong establishment.

"Look, honey," he said, dripping with sarcasm and disrespect, "they're all licensed. Apparently, I have come to the wrong place." He turned toward the door, opening it to walk out.

I wanted so to kick his butt as he exited. In my mind, I did. He had *definitely* come to the wrong place. What an insult! I wore scrub tops just to give people peace of mind. People show more respect when in a type of uniform.

I hoped I would never see him again.

A Little Stiff Neck

Shortly after that incident, another fellow came in as I happened to be in the front of the office, and I watched as he drove into the parking lot, got out of his car, and walked toward the door.

I guessed his age to be about sixty-five. He came in, introduced himself, and asked to get a massage for his stiff neck.

I asked his age; he told me forty-five.

"Sure," I said. "Is this work-related?"

He tried to turn his head but it was locked and stiff. I asked how he could drive without turning his head. He showed me how turning his head and shoulders were the only movements he was able to do.

"Well, let's see what I can do for you. I think it's possible I can help."

As I loosened the muscles of his neck and shoulders, and was able to get some slight movement of the head from the shoulders, I asked questions about him to get a better understanding of his condition.

He worked at a computer all day and would go home, have dinner, watch TV, and go to bed, and the next day, his wife would fix his breakfast, and then he would go to work. That was his routine.

"Do you get any exercise whatsoever?" I asked him.

"No."

He had no reason to turn his head except to drive, and it was locked into place and hurting. I asked him to come back so we could get him loosened up. He came to see me four times in two weeks. When he came in the fifth time, he was so proud and showed me he could turn his head.

"Look! It's working and getting better," he said with jubilance as he turned his head slightly one way, then the other, with ease but not overly as I would have liked.

"That's great!" I said. "Now we can reduce the treatments to once a week, then to once a month, and you'll be feeling much better."

He stopped coming after two months.

Six months later, he called for an appointment, and when he stepped inside the door, he couldn't turn his head again.

"It didn't work. Your treatment doesn't work. I can't turn my head anymore."

"But it did work," I said to him in my defense. "Do you get gas for your car weekly and oil changes to maintain your car regularly?" I asked.

"Yeah," he said.

"Then, with the type of work you do, you also need routine maintenance to keep your neck and body moving."

He did one more treatment with me, and I could tell his muscle memory was positive and that it wouldn't take long to get him moving again, but then I didn't see him again until about a year later. He came in, and I recognized and greeted him.

"Good to see you again. Hope you've been well." I said.

"My wife and daughter have been getting massages from you and think highly of you. So, I thought I would give you another try."

"Well, I think your wife and daughter are wonderful too. I'm always happy to see them and glad to help."

He had a couple of treatments and then just stopped coming altogether. His wife and daughter continued coming occasionally until I left that office. I didn't see him again.

A Bold Request

"Lynn, I would like you to be topless."

I laughed, as I thought he was joking. I didn't believe what I had heard, or maybe misunderstood, and shrugged it off.

This client had a standing weekly appointment. He managed a local restaurant chain store and was pleasant, in his midthirties, married with kids, and in good shape. During what became his last massage with me . . . he asked me, out of the blue, to take my top off.

"No, I'm serious! I'm naked on this table, and I want you to be topless while you massage me. If you don't . . . I'm not coming back," he said threateningly.

"Well," I said. "First of all, you are not totally naked, you are legally covered with a towel. Why would you ask me such a thing?" I stood, listening.

"We are comfortable with each other. I like your massages, obviously, or I wouldn't be here. I would just like for *you* to be topless. I think it is only fair," he said.

"Well then," I said with agitated seriousness. "I'm not taking my top off for you or anyone else. We are almost finished with your massage, or we can stop right now and you don't owe me a dime, and you can leave!"

"No, Lynn, please finish. But I won't be back," he said sternly.

"Okay, that's fine with me. I'm sorry you would ask me such a thing." I finished the massage.

To this day, every time I see this chain restaurant, I think of that time and that guy and have never stepped foot in one. And . . . I never saw him again either.

The Knee Guy!

The knee guy came in wearing shorts and a T-shirt, trying to navigate through the door on crutches, unable to put any pressure on his right leg—specifically the knee—agonizing in pain.

"Anything you can do to alleviate the pain in my knee would be greatly appreciated," he said, fighting back tears.

"What did you do to cause it? Injury or sport?" I asked.

"No. I may need a knee replacement, they tell me. It started getting sore one day and it has been getting worse. I don't know what happened to it. Now I've lost my job as a construction worker. I'm a heavy-equipment operator and can't work without my legs. My wife is a teacher, and it will be three months for her insurance to kick in so we will have health insurance. I had good insurance but now I don't. Can you help me?"

"Did you bump it or get a spider bite, or what? How did it start? Any information is helpful for me to help you. I can see you are in a great deal of pain; we'll get your paperwork done later. Let's go on back to a treatment room."

I helped him back into the massage room and onto the table. He laid faceup, and I tried putting a pillow under his knee. That didn't help either. I tried to make him comfortable, but his knee was inflamed and swollen, yet there was no broken skin. I looked for a bite but didn't see anything.

"Okay," I said, "I'm not sure what to do either, but let's try a couple of things to get your pain level down."

"Oh, please, yes, this is killing me," he pleaded. "Jump on it if you want. And don't touch anywhere else; I'm fine everywhere else. Spend all your time on the knee . . . please. Do whatever you need to do to ease the pain so I can be out of here."

As I began to massage his knee and leg, I noticed how the pain had radiated all over his body. I drew the inflammation from the knee area. He wanted me to be as aggressive as necessary to ease his pain, but I could only rely on my instincts for this one.

Maria? I need your help for this one! I quietly said to myself.

"Well . . . I have a problem with that," I said. "And what I mean by that is your whole body is in trauma. I understand your situation, that money is tight right now, it's three months before Christmas, you've lost your job, and you're looking at a knee replacement. But I won't work just on your bad leg unless you let me massage the good one too!"

"No, the left leg is okay. I just want the right one looked after."

"Look," I said, trying to sound sympathetic and non-threatening, "I'll make a deal with you. Let's work on the bad leg, and if I can help ease the pain, will you consider letting me work the other one?"

"Okay, okay," he somewhat reluctantly agreed.

After about twenty minutes, I heard him give out a big sigh and a slight moan as his knee relaxed for the first time. Then I asked, "Pain better?"

"Yes," he said, as if he could breathe.

"Oh good . . . that was challenging for me. Now, let's give that bad leg a break and work on the good one."

"You really don't have to. It's fine really," he said.

"If you let me, I'm going to prove to you that your support leg needs it as much, if not more, than your hurt one," I said.

So, with that, he let me massage both feet then I worked up the calves of both legs to the knees, then the lateral thighs to the hip, eventually getting to the hands and shoulders, neck, and then he turned over so I could rub his lower back.

I tried to explain to him that his good leg and the rest of his body was traumatized by working double to support him while in pain. Plus, the walking with crutches and balancing on one leg had his back, shoulders, and arms aching as well. All the while he moaned, surprised by how he hurt in places he didn't know hurt, but he was thankful afterward.

When I finished, I helped him sit up in case he got dizzy. Then I left the room to wash my hands and told him I would see him in the outer office when he got himself together.

I was waiting in the outer office as he slowly walked out with a slight limp, as if guarding his leg in case the pain retuned. He reached for his wallet then realized he forgot something.

"I forgot my crutches!" And immediately did an about-turn to go retrieve them.

"Oh, yes please. It's not good advertising to have them sitting in a room," I said with a slight laugh.

He was smiling as he paid, thanked me for my services, and carried his crutches as he walked out on his own two feet in disbelief after the pain he had endured.

While cleaning the room and laying out fresh sheets on the table, I rethought the whole scenario of what just happened. I was thankful I was able to help him purely working by instinct on that knee and silently said a prayer of thanks to any higher power.

I returned to the front office to deal with paperwork and realized I didn't get his name. Nothing!

I can't call him later to check on his condition. How will I ever know what happens? Maybe he'll come back?

It's just that when someone sees me in his condition, I liked to follow up with a call. Not everyone, but this one I would have liked to follow up on, and I had nothing.

I thought of him for a whole year and never saw him until one day, I was visiting in the office with the owner and another therapist, and a man and his teenage son stepped in the door, both wearing baseball caps low over their eyes.

"Can we help you?" we asked.

The older of the two looked at me and pointed his right index finger almost in my face.

"You," he said, almost accusingly. "You helped me once!"

I leaned in closer to get a look at him under the bill of his cap.

"You're the guy with the knee!" I exclaimed.

"Yes," he said smiling. "That's right!"

"Oh my! I have wondered about you. You were in such pain that day, and I was going to call you afterward, but I forgot to get your name and number, and you walked out carrying your crutches. I was hoping to see you again, but you never came back. How are you? Did you get the knee replacement? You look great!" I was talking so fast and realized the others in the room looked bewildered!

"No, I didn't get the knee replacement," he said. "I ended up having surgery on my knee as I had an infection in it. We don't know how, but the doctor opened it up, cleaned out the infection, put in some antibiotic medicine, and closed it up, and I was back to work. All is well. Thanks to your help, I was able to get through it."

"That is absolutely wonderful," I said. "We love happy endings like that. "Around here we have to be careful about saying that." He looked questioning.

"Happy endings," I said. And we all laughed.

He had come in, inquiring about getting some therapy for his son, who was growing up and getting into sports. He had remembered me helping him with confidence and thought that his son would be in good hands.

Heart Transplant Recipient

Another person I met while working at that office, whom I found fascinating, was a mature gentleman who drove up in a large limousine. This small-statured, bald gentleman drove up in front of our office and parked in a handicap space. I wondered if he was a chauffeur at first, as he got out dressed in a casual, short-sleeve shirt and shorts, looking out of character for a limo.

When he came in the first time, we introduced ourselves and I asked a few questions. He expressed the need for a massage because he was experiencing discomfort on one side of his back, near his shoulder blade, and was looking for relief.

As I began massaging him, I noticed the scar on the front of his chest. Probably from bypass surgery, I surmised. He mainly wanted someone to press the one spot in his back to release a pressure there.

I asked about the scar, and he told me he was a heart transplant recipient of nine years! I was surprised and honored at the same time. I had never met a heart recipient before and therefore was concerned about the reason for his pain. In my experiences, with bypass or any time a chest is cracked open, there is a chance for thoracic outlet syndrome and/or displacement of a rib which causes the symptoms he was experiencing.

He came each week, once or twice a week, just to get relief and seemed to be getting worse. I referred him to a chiropractor friend of mine, as I thought he would be able to help.

He said he didn't believe in those people but finally agreed to go after a couple of months of suggesting. Dr. B. was able to give him the relief he needed, but it would only last a short while and slip out again. But he did have a renewed respect for chiropractors.

Shortly afterward, the gentleman developed cancer caused by the rejection meds he had to take. He then left for the Cleveland Clinic, and I wondered if I would ever see him again. Six months later, he returned driving a new limo (his gift to himself for beating cancer).

Shortly thereafter, I was in the office less due to my mom's illness, and I would take time off to visit her in Ohio, sometimes weeks at a time. However, he continued to come to our office for massages with one of the other therapists.

Chapter 17
Competition? Business?

Teamwork

While working at that office, the owner brought in another massage therapist, Carrie, who was great to work with and helped to balance the office. I had certain days, the owner had certain days, and she had certain days.

I enjoyed working with other therapists, and I had already worked in a spa atmosphere with six other therapists. Like anything else, it was what you brought into the practice. Knowledge and techniques are your skills. Massage and bodywork shouldn't be competitive.

When you work in a spa or office, some people will try different therapists before they find that one, special person they like and they want to stick with that therapist. That is, if they get regular massages. Some people don't care or they are getting the occasional massage and anyone will do.

I've made house calls carrying my table from one house to another. Let me tell you, that isn't easy.

A couple living in our neighborhood asked me to come to their house to do massages on both husband

and wife. Afterward, they told me they had been receiving massages from another therapist for several years but decided they would like to get regular massages from me. It was time for a change. I was honored to hear that, and we set forth to plan time each month.

About a week later, I received a phone call from them saying they wouldn't be needing me after all because their regular therapist broke down and cried and pleaded to not let her go because she needed the money and would be devastated if she didn't get it.

I told myself then I would never do that to anyone. If a client wanted to see someone else, it would be their choice, and I wouldn't shame them like that.

I had a few regular clients who would come to see me, and after the new massage therapist came in, we settled into a routine together. It was nice having someone dependable who could handle my clients if necessary and we could cover for each other. That's teamwork. I was confident our business in that little office was going to get busier.

One day, the owner asked to talk to me.

"What's up?"

"Well," she began as we both sat down. "Carrie, the new therapist, has been here a few weeks now, and I need to tell you that one of your regular clients has asked for her instead of you, and I know how you must be feeling right now when you hear this news. It can be upsetting or cause jealousy, and we all go through it."

"Okay," I said. "And just what am I supposed to be feeling? What are you talking about?" She just knew I would be upset, but I wasn't.

"Look," I said. "Carrie is a good therapist, and we all

want what is best for our clients, and we trade massages with each other. I have no qualms about anyone asking for her. I am a good therapist and confident in my work and knowledge. There are a few people I prefer not to do also, but we bear with it. It's really okay with me!"

You can also feel thankful. Sure, we build clientele and a rapport with people, but occasionally we all like to move on and build more relationships and can't be everything to all people. Some clients have a way of draining energy and leave the therapist drained. I speak to hairdressers that feel the same way. Some people will energize you and others can drain you.

I certainly learned a lot working in that small office.

It made me feel better that, when I left that office, I didn't leave anyone hanging, and my clients were taken care of. With my mother ill in Ohio and me making trips back and forth to see her, having the extra therapist there was a blessing. It wasn't long after that we moved, but I heard later that Carrie and the owner had a falling out and she started her own business elsewhere, taking clients with her.

Such is the massage therapy business.

Pregnant or NOT?

When I think back at some of the clients in that office, I always remember two in particular. Two ladies, unknown to each other, came in the same day at different times after making appointments for massages. One lady was eight and a half months pregnant, nearing her due date, and asked if I knew any tricks or trigger points to help get her contractions started. She wanted to have the baby and whatever I could do, she'd be grateful.

"Well," I told her. "No promises, but I know there are some trigger points around the ankles that may work. But you also have to promise me not to have it here! I don't want to deliver any baby."

After I massaged her neck and shoulders, lower back, and feet, she felt better and was heading home. I was glad to get her out the door just in case she did start labor. Right after she left, my next client came in asking me: "Is there anything you can do to help me get pregnant?"

I stood there for a moment with a strange look on my face as I digested what she had just asked me. I giggled slightly as she realized how she sounded.

"Well, you know what I mean," she said shyly. "My husband and I are trying to get pregnant and don't seem to be having any luck. We thought we could try massage therapy before going to any drastic measures."

"Well," I said with a laugh. "The lady who just left asked if I could get her to start labor to have her baby. Then you come in asking if I can help you get pregnant." Of course, we both chuckled.

"Maybe some energy is still here from her to help you," I said joking, but this was not a laughing matter.

I massaged her body to get her relaxed and did some trigger-point therapy around the legs, ankles, and feet for what I thought could help with her request. I asked if she was sure she was not pregnant at the time, and she said she was sure. With that, I gave her a mild, abdominal massage as that would sometimes help. I said a prayer while I massaged her as well. That never hurts.

"I can't promise anything, but I tried my best to help accommodate. I wish you luck."

I never saw either lady after that day. I don't know if what I did worked or not.

Strange how people come in and out of our lives, and I wonder about some of them as I write.

The Power Company Men

We were mostly appointment only, and it was interesting to ponder what a day might bring, as I drove in sometimes just to wait for a walk-in.

One such day, as I was watching the traffic go by, three electrical trucks with the cherry pickers on them came roaring in, following each other. We had electric, or at least *our* office did. *Perhaps someone called the power company about something,* I thought to myself.

Three men climbed down out of two of the truck cabs, and one ran around to the other side of the cab as all the guys ran to help a fellow lineman out and carried him to our door and into the office. They were all young men helping their friend. The first guy that came in ahead of the others asked if I had time to help their friend. They were wet, dirty, and muddy.

"What happened?" I inquired. "And shouldn't you take him to the ER?" As they carried him through the door, the small reception room becoming full. The others waited outside.

"He slipped and pulled his back but didn't want to go to the ER. Said he wanted to come and see you!"

"Oh dear. Get him in the second treatment room, please, and I'll see what I can do," I told them, as he was in definite pain. I felt like a mom to these young fellows. At least Mom instincts kicked in at times like these. A perk of being a massage therapist is that I get to have my hands on these strong, good-looking, beefy bodies, but when Mom-mode kicks in, they are little boys.

"Look, ma'am," one of them said, "we'll leave him with you because we have to get back to work. How long do you think it will take?"

"Please give me at least an hour," I said. The guys all

collaborated a few minutes as he was trying to sit on the massage table and take off his shirt and boots.

I was trying to keep things comfortable for him and asked what he had done. From the look of it, he had pulled his low lumbar and SI joints. I tried to take some of the trauma out and got him calmed down. He felt better after an hour of working the tissues of his back. He said he felt better and would ice it and promised me that if he didn't feel noticeably better, he would see a doctor.

I felt confident it was a pull and he hadn't fallen or broken anything. Only one truck came back to retrieve their colleague, and he was able to walk out on his own. He came to see me a day later, and then each week for about a month, and was soon better. Some things were meant to be. I often wonder what would have happened if I hadn't been there that day.

Dress UP!

There were cross-dressers, mostly men, who would come in occasionally.

One such guy said to me, "You ladies always have all the fun of dressing up."

He told me he was an executive of a bank, and his wife would give him a pass for one weekend a month. He would go somewhere—like a large hotel with a pool—to dress up in drag, as he liked showing off his legs and wear stockings, miniskirts, shoes, handbags, and wigs. It was his little secret from the business world and his family. He said he had a high-stress job and needed massages as well, and this was part of his outlet.

Shhh! Don't Judge!

Another strange, weird incident with a walk-in was a guy who asked me if everything was confidential, Of course, I agreed, and he proceeded to tell me he had bruises and red marks on his body. When I inquired about what had happened, he told me he had an evening with a dominatrix. He watched me to see what my reaction would be. I tried not to react, but I'm sure I did.

I try not to judge people. But when they spring this kind of news on me, I can't help letting my feelings show. My eyebrows had to have gone up. I wondered if he gained pleasure from my reaction or if he thought I'd offer the same.

I let him know, "Whatever floats your boat, man. But not my cup of tea. My lotions have arnica in them, and that helps with the healing of bruises on the skin."

"Okay," he said.

I didn't know if he thought I would call authorities and report it or if he just wanted to see my reaction. He was a mature, adult man, I guessed in his late thirties, and he let me know he had a really good gal this time and that he was happy with the result.

"That's nice," I said. I didn't want to know what that result was.

Honestly, I didn't see much bruising at all, only a few red marks across his back but nothing noticeable like cuts or blood.

I never saw him again, thankfully.

The Subdivision

The subdivision where we lived in Florida was part of a resort that had a large clubhouse with pools, a spa, restaurants, and a motel.

The resort was under construction when we moved there, and we purchased a condo and settled in. It was the thing to do, it seemed, but we had never lived in a condo before and really didn't like it. I had to get my feet on the ground, so we purchased a lot on the lake and then a small mobile home, added a car port and a screened lanai, and we felt more at home.

During the winter months, the snowbirds came to these resorts, and I met another massage therapist who was a snowbird. She and her husband would spend winters there six months of the year. Their house was about five houses away from ours, and the lots were small. So, during those months, we agreed to trade massages.

That was a great time for both of us. Every Sunday morning at nine a.m., you would see one of us in our bathrobe and slippers walking to the others' house for a massage. One week, she would come to my house for me to massage her, then the next week, I would slip into a robe and slippers and be out the door, breathing in the fresh, morning air, and take a short walk to a waiting table. Massage table that is!

We preferred working in our own environment, setting up the table, lotions, sheets. It worked out great.

As that resort grew, I eventually decided to apply to work there when the spa was up and running. That, too, brought some interesting clientele.

I was one of the first massage therapist hired. I started around the pool so people could see that we had massage therapists. It was good advertising.

Chapter 18
Upscale Resort and Spa

Massage opportunities were plentiful in Florida, either to work or receive. There were many schools and massage therapists there.

Working at a resort was always busy, and I had an opportunity to work at one near Tampa. It was new and it's always interesting to work at a new start-up. In the beginning, I was outside around the pool, under an umbrella or a palapa (that is an umbrella made out of palm leaves). The pool was a very large, free form with islands within and palm trees in and all around, and at one end was a waterfall with an alcove to swim under.

Each day, weather permitting, I would roll my table out to an area assigned to me at the opposite end of the pool from the waterfall and set up and have a white board for people to sign up for times to have massages. Outdoor massages are different with other people around, being in the open for all to see. When outdoors around a pool, there was always tropical music playing and sometimes even live music. I, and the other therapists, would be out of the way but scattered around the perimeter of the pool area. With the palm trees and warm breezes, some likened it to a cruise ship or island.

One couple that would come daily to the pool would select a lounge chair at the same spot each day. From that vantage point, they could see all around the pool. One day, they came over to me asking about massage therapy. They had retired recently from up north and moved to Florida for retirement. Their daughter was going to massage therapy school back in Michigan, and they said they had been watching me each day and wondered about the benefits of massage. I told them of some of the health benefits of massage and they replied that that's what the daughter says. So, having never had a massage, the husband signed up. The wife decided to watch and get hers later.

"My daughter says I need a deep tissue massage," he said.

"Well . . . I don't recommend a deep tissue for anyone's first massage. I suggest something a little less invasive but thorough. A deep tissue can cause detoxification, make you sore, or even ill since you've never had one. Start slow and then do a follow-up in a week or so."

"My daughter says I should have a deep tissue, and that's what I want," he repeated.

"Okay," I said. "But you must promise me not to drink much alcohol today, and lots of water is a must to keep you from being ill or sore or dehydrated."

"Yeah, okay," he agreed.

But he did not heed my advice, as I didn't see them for about three days. The wife came out the fourth day and walked over to talk with me. She told me he had gotten very ill with flu-like symptoms and even went to the doctor. The following week, they came out again, and he was still drained of energy from being so ill and not drinking anything but water. I went over to them and told him I was sorry he had gotten so ill.

"You probably don't want to hear this now, but you should have a follow-up massage to help finish detoxing you to cleanse the rest of your tissues. It will help you feel better, and it will feel totally different than the first one. And you will be healthier. I like to think I did you a favor by working your tissues before you had a worse illness."

"Yeah, if it weren't for my daughter, I probably would be mad at you, but she said the same damn thing. I don't know but sign me up. I just hope you all know what you're talking about." I had to smile.

After working on him again, he definitely could feel the difference. A few days later, he agreed he was on the verge of being ill—seriously ill—and felt like a million dollars after that second massage. The wife then got hers, which was not deep tissue, and then a follow-up. They were both happy and became advocates for me when asked about massage. They recommended me to several others who visited the resort. I even overheard them telling several other visiting patrons that they highly recommended me.

A few years later, their daughter became a massage therapist at the resort!

Now, we offer all kinds of different types of massage and spa services. Like body wraps, Vichy showers, couples' massages and synchronized massages, two-handed and four-handed, hydraulic tables, and hot cabbies with warm towels. This farm girl had been privy to all these things in one place, and I got to learn a little more about how the other half lives by working there and being a part of this.

I remember not long after graduation from massage school, I received invitations from a few upscale resorts and spas to come fill out applications and interview to work for them. Most of these were well-known resorts in other states. I guess they were looking for a few good therapists.

Sometimes while poolside, people would come up and talk to me or ask questions while I worked on someone. This could be considered rude, but when I rolled my table out in the morning and set up under an umbrella or a palapa, it did lend itself to being vulnerable for questions. It was something to get used to. Most of the massages people wanted poolside were for relaxation while lounging. Not too much "bodywork" going on here. Everyone was wearing swimsuits and lying on the top sheet without a drape.

There was always the guys and some gals who would get a massage but wanted me to use their suntan or sunscreen lotion or oil so they didn't have to. Some people could get very creative when it came to applying sunscreen or lotions.

Depending on the time of year or the weather conditions, I would set up late in the morning during cooler months or earlier in the morning during hotter months, before it got too hot.

If the temperature would get cool in the afternoon and my fingers started getting cold, I had to pack up. I cannot work with cold hands, and a chill would affect my hands immediately.

I started to pack up one afternoon as I felt the temperature drop. This lady insisted I massage her. I tried telling her a massage would also drop her core body temperature and make her feel cool. She started to get chilled, and I covered her with a top sheet, but my fingers were like icicles and felt like boney fingers. I hurried the massage along to get her done, but it was a lesson taken.

One More Please!

One beautiful, sunny day, around four in the afternoon, as most people were calling it a day and leaving the pool area to go home or to their room, I was starting to pack up to also go home, when a friend came up and asked me to stay a little longer. They had a friend who was on her way and had sent word for me to please give her a head and neck massage to help a migraine.

She showed up shortly thereafter. The sun had lowered behind a cloud, the palm trees swayed in the breeze, the music was off, and we had just the sounds of the waterfall across the other side of the pool.

As she came up to lie down on the massage table, I could see the pain in her face. I asked that she lie down faceup, and I sat down to put my hands under her head and neck, lightly massaging under her shoulders and holding her head in both my hands. She started moaning and swaying her head back and forth as I began to feel tingling in both my hands. Slowly, I could feel the tingling sensation move into my fingers and wrist and up into my forearms and then to my elbows. Now it had to stop. *Stop at the elbows, no further*, I told myself.

"How is your headache now?" I asked.

"Oh! It's feels like you are draining it out though my ears," she said, with a light moan.

"Well, you are right, but I need to step away for about two minutes. Are you okay with that?" I asked.

"Oh, yes," she said. "My headache is gone."

"Stay right here, I'll be right back," I said again.

I got up and walked straight over to the nearest palm tree, about five feet away, and put both hands on the tree, channeling the tingling from my arms into the tree. I could feel the tingling in both my arms up to my elbows begin to drain as it absorbed into the tree, freeing me of the pain I had taken from the lady on my table. I then went back to her and massaged her head, neck, and shoulders again. The whole treatment lasted approximately thirty minutes, then she was up and smiling.

I love these happenings. You never know when these things will work or not. They just happen, and I smile and feel blessed that it does.

One Day That Will Be Me!

One day, a fellow came up to me while I was working on someone and said, "Wow, an outdoor massage. That's cool. You know, I had a massage last week at another resort we were visiting from a lady who was sixty-nine years old. The strength she had was incredible and the best massage I've ever had."

"I hope that will be me some day!" I responded.

Bodywork and Art

With the constant turnover of clientele each week at a resort, you see all kinds of bodies and lots of skin, especially around the pool.

Surgery scars, breast reductions, enhancements, and reconstruction after a mastectomy, as well as face lifts, hair transplants, toupees, tummy tucks, butt lifts, liposuction, and various other nips and tucks. As a massage therapist, we see it all. Not to mention the shoulder, knee, and hip replacements. That is life nowadays. Let's not forget the piercings and tattoos . . .

While massaging a body builder, I noticed the calves of his legs had a strange bubble-pillow feeling in both of them. When I asked him about it, he told me they were implants as he had difficulty building up that part of his body.

Heat Stroke

One very hot day, as I was working on a client, I felt like I needed to excuse myself from the massage table, as I was feeling a little nauseous. I had been drinking water, but I could feel it setting in my stomach.

I was about twenty feet away from the edge of the large pool. Tropical music was playing, and the crowd was large that day. The ladies' restroom and shower was about twenty-five feet from my station, so I excused myself and went to the ladies' room to splash water on my face.

There were several stalls inside, and all were empty, so I leaned up against the concrete-block wall and slid down the wall until I was sitting on the floor to cool myself.

Suddenly, I heard the door open and someone came in. It was one of the waitresses, and she saw me leaning up against the wall, pivoted, and went back out. I wondered why and thought I had better get back out on deck. So, I walked back out to the outside shower, untied my sarong, and dropped it on the pavers then stepped into the shower. Wearing a swimsuit, I stood under the shower to cool off then stepped out, picked up the sarong, and wrapped it back around me soaking wet then went back to finish the massage.

Ten more minutes, I said to myself. I had ten more minutes, and I would be finished with George, then I can pack up and go home. *I'm not feeling well, I need to go home. Ten more minutes.* I approached the table, and he was still lying there, probably sleeping. I apologized for leaving, but I had felt a little ill and was better now, so we were just about finished. It wasn't five minutes later when he asked me if I was feeling okay.

"No, George, I'm not," I remember saying.

"Do you need to lie down, Lynn?" he asked.

"Yes, George. I'm sorry, but I feel faint and need to lie down." At that point, he was lying facedown and had turned to look at me but got off the table as I fell onto it. He helped me to lie down, lifting my feet so I was centered on the table, not falling off it. He then looked around to ask someone to help. Ernie was called and seemed to be right there. I don't remember how long it was, but the waitress who saw me in the restroom earlier had gone to get a bag of ice and was on her way back. She dumped a whole bag of ice on top of me.

"I know the signs of heat stroke!" she was saying. "I saw her in the restroom earlier, and I went to get her some ice knowing she was about to pass out."

"Should we call 911?" I heard someone ask. Ernie and George were standing over me.

"No. Please," I said faintly. "I'm all right. I've been drinking water to stay hydrated, but it just stays in my stomach instead of being absorbed. Just let me get my stuff together and go home to cool down."

I apologized to George and told him I would not charge him for today. He insisted on paying me since I was almost done with him anyway. I said I would make it up to him next time. He and his wife lived close and liked to come to the resort on weekends and get massages.

A couple other massage therapists also came to my rescue and gave me some juice and celery to eat. Celery has a natural salt content that helps to absorb fluids to hydrate the body. I ate a lot of celery from that day forward, plus there are a lot of good health benefits from eating celery.

Ernie folded up the massage table while I sat. Others helped carry everything to the car, then he drove me home, and I took a few days off. It took me nearly two weeks to get over that heat stroke!

I limited my outdoor massages after that. The new spa opened just feet from the pool, so I didn't need to work in that heat.

So, I moved inside with the air conditioning. There was a sauna and a steam room with a manicure and pedicure room and tropical murals on the walls. Several rooms doubled for facials and massage with hydraulic tables. One room for couple massages. A large room with a wet table and Vichy shower for body scrubs. This sounded like a lavish place and it was. We had six massage therapists, two being men. Poolside massages were only done now by preference or special request.

* * *

A few months before I had my heat stroke, I was approached and asked if I would manage the spa, and I was flattered at the idea, but had felt it was too much for me to take on that amount of responsibility. I wanted to do what I do best—massages—and have the flexibility to work at my own pace without that kind of responsibility.

For me, it was a place to work, learn, and earn. No more corporate world for me. We negotiated a contract for earnings and percentages, then signed all necessary documents to keep everyone legal and, hopefully, happy.

I like to think of myself as a team player; I love working with other people. I believe when we treat everyone with respect, we get respect in return. Since I was one of the first to work there, I welcomed others as they came on board, and we would help each other when timing or workload became busy.

We had one person at the front desk taking appointments

for everyone. Learning the new computer system and keeping staff and clients on time was challenging.

When the new manager asked me what the most clients I'd ever done in a day was, I told him eight, but that was not something that could be done on a daily basis, A break between clients was necessary.

Oh well, all he heard was eight and proceeded to instruct that appointments be scheduled every hour, for eight hours per therapist. That's not how it works with this profession!

Unknown to me was, this guy had never managed a spa or salon; therefore, when he had presented his business plan to management, it had been an unrealistic goal. Therapists would be expected to do eight massages per day, not accounting for superficial or deep tissue massages. We had therapists who specialized in other modalities also. Every service had its own price. Times were cut from thirty to twenty-five, sixty to fifty, and ninety to eighty minutes respectively. He expected us to work like robots or machines on an assembly line.

When I asked him if he ever had a massage, he said no. Then I asked that he let me give him a massage so he would have the experience to learn something about massage and how we work. His reply was he knew what he was doing — which was insulting since he never had a massage — and wouldn't have someone like me touching him!

I assumed he was referring to my age.

He was gone in a few weeks for mismanagement and a complaint of inappropriate behavior from the woman he received a massage from after he fired her.

Management then hired someone who would listen to its staff and manage accordingly.

People make the difference so don't abuse them. We know there is a bottom line.

Fiftieth Anniversary Couple

One weekend, a couple came in to celebrate their fiftieth wedding anniversary. We had specials for such events. We even had a massage room just for couples. On special occasions, they would have a massage together, and afterward, we would bring in a bottle of champagne and a fruit and cheese tray with chocolate-dipped strawberries for them to enjoy. They could have it in the room or have it outside overlooking the pool after their massage.

But this couple had a special request. This couple, being in their seventies, asked for a handsome, shirtless, young man for her, and he requested two ladies to massage him for an hour—dressed, of course. One of our male therapists, Bob, filled the bill very well—with his fortysomething, buff, bare chest, and also was an instructor at the nearby college—and was happy to take off his shirt for the lady while giving her a massage. And Dina and I were selected to massage the gentleman.

As we made introductions, the elder gentleman looked Dina and I up and down and asked, "Who will be doing my feet?"

"That would be me, sir," I said, looking down at this five-foot-five elder man.

"Well, I need to show you something first," he said, looking up at me, standing at five-foot-eight. He looked down and grabbed his pants legs and pulled them up, exposing his ankles for me to see. He had already removed his shoes and socks, and I saw, very clearly, two black and blue ankles from an old injury.

"Wow, how long ago was that injury?" I asked.

He looked up at me with a bit of a crooked, sideways gaze and said, "Oh, about forty year ago," with a bit of a Boston accent. He continued, "I was young, and they had to cut me out of a car. The doctor wanted to amputate them to get me out. He told me I probably would never be able to walk again anyway. But I begged him and said that didn't matter. I wanted to keep my feet."

"Well, it looks like you are a walking miracle, and I will be glad to work on them for you. Just let me know if I need to do anything special."

After that, we left the room and let the couple get undressed to get on the massage tables. We knocked on the door to enter the room to proceed with our massages. Talk was light, and Dina did all the massage on his body while I explored this man's feet. He was honestly a walking miracle, as not a bone in those feet were in their proper place.

His feet were mostly black and blue due to no blood supply. They were mostly skin stuck to bone and only had a few pink areas around a couple of toes with circulation. Apparently just enough to keep his feet attached. But the real miracle was he had learned to walk with them and lived to celebrate fifty years of marriage.

When we go into a room like that, with several therapists working together, it is kept quiet with no verbal conversation unless an occasional question to the client about pressure or asking them to turn over. There are a few hand signals to each other to help coordinate timing of turning over to have both clients turn and complete the massages simultaneously.

Afterward, they were both delighted with the work we did on them, and he complimented me on a job well done. He said no one had ever gotten into the nooks and crannies of his feet the way I did and was very happy.

Their champagne and tray of goodies arrived and was waiting outside the door to be brought in as we were leaving.

After we left the room and were walking down the hall, I

asked Bob how it went with the lady. He said she slept the whole time. We all smiled at each other. They thanked me for being a reflexologist who made him happy. We did good and were happy to have made an anniversary memorable.

Fun Stuff

Two couples vacationing together requested the couples' massage room altogether. They vacationed together *and* they got massaged together! Us massage therapists stood together in a circle, discussing how to make this work.

"Can we fit two more tables in the room?" someone asked.

We managed to move two more tables into the one room. We tried to angle or turn it in different ways but that didn't work. We wound up just lining the tables up and dressed them with clean sheets and pillows as we talked.

"Who's massaging? That's four people and four therapists! We will be butt cheek to butt cheek in here. We need to coordinate how we start and finish. Does male or female matter on who does who? This is funny!"

"They are on vacation anyway. Probably new to them also!"

"The women want men therapists, and the men want women."

"Cool beans, we can handle that. Love the plan!"

"Let's make the most of it. Turn up the air, it will get hot in there with eight bodies!"

Then we went back into the hallway to greet our new challenges.

We exchanged handshakes and laughter, and then the therapists stepped out of the room as the clients got on the tables.

We were all trying to gather our composure before going into the room so as not to laugh at this new challenge.

We were all talking together about how to begin on the right sides of the tables and we'd move accordingly around to the left. We got quiet as we lined up and, respectfully, walked into that massage room of four tables with two men and two women.

We therapists tried to keep quiet and keep to our hand signals. Their giggles continued for the first thirty minutes, and then they calmed down. The guys fell asleep as usual, with a little snoring, and the ladies talked, as usual. We had to keep our coordination from bumping into each other while we were cheek to cheek. We coordinated the halfway-time turnover with hand signals and compressed giggles. Then we did it again when it was getting time to finish everyone at the same time. It was all fun!

No More Backache!

A lady executive came into the spa for a general massage and told me she had a constant low backache and had trouble sleeping at night because of it. She took pain meds every night before bed so she could sleep. Of course, when she told me this, I wanted to help alleviate some of that stress she was experiencing.

I structured my massage on her to get her relaxed then immediately targeted her lower back and sacroiliac. She told me she had gotten massages before, but I did some different techniques that helped her back pain. She came back the next day and was thrilled to tell me that, for the first time in two years, she didn't take a pain pill before going to bed, and she slept great! She then rescheduled another massage with me for the next day before having to leave to return home. Unfortunately, she called in and had an emergency at home and had to leave before I saw her again.

About a week later, she called the spa and left the name of the city where she lived and her email address for me, asking if I knew of any therapists near her that were versed in the massage techniques I used. I did some research and did forward a name to her via email. I never heard from her again after that.

I think of her and often wonder how she is.

A Candlelight Massage!

Once during an approaching hurricane, the resort was all but empty of guests. One couple had flown in from somewhere a few days before and had nowhere to go due to the weather. They had scheduled massages, and we were in the safest place underground. Everyone had gone home and what few were left were sheltering in the clubhouse bar areas. What luck!

I told the manager and the couple if they agreed, I would stay and give them their massages as most staff had gone home.

"I'd rather be busy than not. We are in a safe place, so why not?" What we didn't know or expect was the power to go out.

I lived on the resort too, and that was our safest place. It was pitch black in the spa as it was underground. We lit candles and set them in the room.

I gave the man his massage first. The woman was out in the waiting room. No music, just silence. He fell into a deep sleep before I finished him. So, I left a candle in the room, hoping he wouldn't fall off the table. Picking up another candle, I then went to get her from the waiting room, and told her that hubby fell asleep. We looked in on him then went into the next room, leaving all the doors open so we could see the lights, and I massaged her. Just as I was finishing her, he came into the room looking for us. He was a bit groggy from waking from his sleep.

"What perfect timing," I said to him. "Are you all right? You fell into a deep sleep, and I didn't want to wake you." He seemed disoriented.

"How long have I been asleep?" he asked.

"About an hour and a half. Long enough for me to almost finish Trisha. I didn't want to be too far away and hoped you wouldn't fall off the massage table. I didn't have the heart to wake you."

"I don't ever remember sleeping like that. Thank you! And of course, we will pay everything tomorrow when the electric comes back on. I feel incredible."

"Of course. This is an experience you don't get on most vacations," I said.

But the whole thing seemed magical. It became a memory for them too.

A massage by candlelight during a hurricane!

Chapter 19
Vacation in the Dominican Republic

We took a trip to the Dominican Republic one spring for a little R&R, and on our flight there, I told Ernie I was going to splurge and have two massages during the week we were there. He was pleased to hear it!

We had a bungalow right on the beach not far from the tiki bar! The day after we arrived, I saw a massage taking place on the beach in a designated area for massages. What luck for me to get an outdoor massage on the beach, and to top it off, I decided to have *two* massages at once. A four-handed massage for an hour. What a treat! I hadn't had that since I was in school. I hurried to the clubhouse to make my appointment. How exciting!

That night, we had a storm blow through. By morning, it was still very breezy and cool, and outside massage was out of the question. But I was still on for a four-handed, synchronized massage from two ladies. What a treat for me!

During the massage, I asked the ladies questions about their training and how they liked their work. One spoke English and the other didn't. The massage was great! Just what the doctor ordered—figuratively, of course. Afterward, I mentioned I wasn't used to lazing around for a whole week and would be itching to get my hands busy on someone and asked if they would let me give them a massage. They turned me down at first because I was a guest here and they wouldn't dream of having a guest work. They may have thought I didn't want to pay them for their work but I wouldn't dream of not paying them and tipped also. I insisted since they couldn't remember when they last had a massage. Besides, they would be doing me a favor.

The lady who was manager finally agreed, and I was back the next morning to give her a massage. When we went into the room, there were two other therapists coming in to take notes with notebooks. One left shortly after we started.

While I massaged her, she would speak in Spanish to the others to ask what I was doing as they made notes. Then she would translate to me what she was saying to them. And she would ask me questions about a technique I used. It became more of a training and sharing of ideas. It made me happy that I could share my gift as she had with me, and I told her so.

As I was finishing, the gal taking notes left, and I followed soon after to wash my hands. As I walked out of the spa room, she was sitting in a chair and as I passed by her.

I nodded and said, "And tomorrow, it's your turn!" with a smile as I left through the spa doors.

She didn't understand what I said and asked the other gal what I had said. Then the other gal ran out the door behind me and asked if I was really coming back tomorrow.

"Of course! Same time, same place tomorrow!"

The next morning, she was waiting with bated breath.

It is always a pleasure to lift ones' spirits like that. We went into the same little room, just the two of us. She spoke very little English, so the massage went smoothly and quietly.

Afterward, I stopped to talk with the manager again, asking how she was after her massage from the day before. She thanked me again and admitted she was a little sore but in a good way and was genuinely grateful. We gave each other a hug. It had been months since any of them had gotten a massage themselves. She then told me I could have any treatment in the spa they offered at no charge. I thanked her, but I was quite satisfied with my massage from days before but would think about it. Meanwhile, the lady I had just massaged came out of the massage room looking like a rag doll and gave me a hug, and we thanked each other as I left out the spa doors.

It was a special memory for me.

No, I didn't go back for any treatments. It is our gift!

It was a wonderful experience, visiting the island, and I was glad to be back home again, rejuvenated.

Chapter 20
Feeling for Home

I struggled during those years in Florida, as I just didn't feel at home. The heat during summers was grueling, and I felt more at home in the North Georgia Mountains. I was driving a lot to Ohio to check on my mother and decided to look at some houses in Georgia that I could use as a halfway spot to Ohio and back. It would be our summer home, and Florida would be a winter place. Both would be modest so as not to break the bank.

I even thought about trying to start a massage clinic that would be more of clinical type of massage, not spa-like. My massages were more physical, bordering almost like physical therapy.

People are always asking me why I decided to do massage therapy. That reason is to help people manage pain and physical problems they have, not just to feel good.

Most people overlook the real benefits of massage until they experience it. It is so much more than a body rub when the therapist is feeling and isolating individual muscles.

During massage classes, when we studied muscles, the instructor would sometimes ask us to find a certain muscle in the body and draw an outline of it with a marker.

Imagine showering the next morning and looking into the mirror to see outlines of muscles drawn on your back or legs, and the bicep, and triceps of the arms with red crayon. A little different than our anatomy coloring book or looking at a cadaver.

Whiplash Injury

A mother and daughter came to see me for neck issues after they had been rear-ended. Mom was in the driver's seat while the daughter was in the passenger seat. They had stopped at a traffic light and had been looking at each other, talking—mom looking right, daughter looking left. Both had the same injury on opposite sides of their neck. Specific neck muscles needed to be de-traumatized for both ladies.

That's an example of clinical/medical massage after injury versus spa massage for just relaxation. Not saying we didn't do both. Most therapists can feel the tightness of the muscles that need to be targeted for release. Muscles also seem to have a memory and can tighten back up after therapy. Especially on someone who does repetitive actions or has been traumatized.

Those two ladies will always remember the trauma they experienced when they stop at a traffic light.

Remember when you got burned on that stove or curling iron? Now, whenever you accidentally brush against those things, even if you know they are not hot, you'll automatically recoil. That is muscle memory!

My husband and I were visiting friends at a campground. When we got in our car to leave, he was driving and I was in the passenger seat. We didn't see a small tree, and he backed into it hard enough that it threw my head forward and then backward, giving me a neck injury. Nothing severe but it was sore for a long time. To this day, whenever he is backing up with me in the passenger seat, I have a flashback of that injury. My body remembers.

> *When someone hits you from behind, it will throw your head backward first then forward. That's how injuries occur.*

Chapter 21
Moving Back to Georgia —I'm a Half-Back!

Who would've ever thought a gal like me from the Midwest would feel at home in Georgia?

We found a house in a small subdivision in North Georgia. Later, I found out I am now a half-back! I had never heard that terminology before, but I have neighbors who call me that, as most of them are as well! A half-back is a northerner (Ohio, Michigan, Pennsylvania, New York, etc.) who has moved from the North to Florida then decided they didn't like it, so they have moved halfway back. We have the four seasons without the extreme heat or cold snow.

The move was a slow one because we still had the house in Florida, and Ernie was still working in Florida until I was established in Georgia. I traveled back and forth every few weeks and was still visiting my mother in Ohio until we got her settled in at an assisted living facility. I would travel to the Georgia house and stay a few days, then travel to Ohio to visit my mom, then headed back to Georgia again for a few days, then finally back to Florida.

I was sleeping on the floor at first. I wanted to get a feel of the house and think of what colors to paint the walls and what décor to choose. I would spend a week at a time painting and wallpapering and enjoying my solitude. I had no TV, but I did carry my laptop to keep up with emails and news. There weren't any smartphones yet. We purchased the house in the spring of 2006 but didn't move in until spring of 2007, after I had painted and ordered some furniture and appliances.

I found a contractor to do some finishing work in the basement so I would have it for my office. It was perfect. It had a private entrance separate from the rest of the house, with a bathroom, so it was a perfect location and layout for my own business.

I needed to get back to work, build a clientele again. I pondered going back to the resort we worked at before, but I wanted a place of my own, to be an independent. That meant beating the bushes for whatever I could get. I had already scouted different places during the year. But I wanted to open up my own massage clinic. It sounded more clinical instead of a salon or spa. But the economy was going down, and it was not a good time to put forth a new business in a small town. It just didn't feel right. Money was tight for everyone.

I would spend time in the local coffee shop with others, checking in with emails there and meeting some of the locals. A lot of pastors invited me to their churches. Everyone I met would invite me to their church, being the friendly people they were. But I wasn't ready to join any church just yet.

I also met other massage therapists. That's where I was clued in that Georgia had passed a law requiring all massage therapists to be licensed. The law was passed in 2005, unbeknownst to me, but wasn't actually being enforced until the end of May 2007! And if you could get three people to sign and notarize a paper stating you have been doing massage for three or more years, you could be grandfathered in without taking the licensing exam. I had already taken the test six years ago and didn't want to take it again. I made it just under the wire, getting my papers turned in, and now I was legal within the state of Georgia. Now licensed in Florida and Georgia—whew!

I was at the right place and right time for all this to happen. My angels were looking out for me, guiding me in the right direction.

Thank you, Lord!

Chapter 22
Franchise

I answered an ad in the local newspaper of someone looking for a massage therapist. Maybe this would get me started again. It took me a little bit of a drive away, but I thought I would check it out.

Well . . . this ad was for a new business just opening.

I interviewed with the owner of this franchise and decided to give it a try for the experience of it and see how the operation worked.

The owner was young, married with kids, just out of the military, and thought it a good idea, so he opened his own place with one store and was opening a second, hence why he needed more therapists to work for him, although he was not a therapist himself. I thought he had a good thing going for himself. And I thought maybe this was what I should do. He, of course, had to receive a massage from me as part of my interview. He was very impressed with my expertise, and I would be one of the oldest therapists working there. That happened often wherever I went.

I'd give it a month. *Four weeks*, I told myself. I'm sure franchise owners are different. This place was brand new and the people he was bringing in were all vying for positions between the two stores he owned or managed. This felt so different than working with seasoned therapists, as most of these people were kids to me. This was a good place for a therapist to start right after graduating, or someone who didn't know how to or didn't want to market themselves, but I was no expert. After all, I'd been looking for the right place for me. But it didn't take long to know this was going to be a short stint for me.

It was nice to just walk in each day and know the laundry would be done and the massage lotion bottle or jars would be filled and ready to use. I liked my bottles filled with half cream and half lotion for the consistency. We were not to touch any of the inventory as such. Walk in, pick your room for the day and your lotion, and go to work. Pay is minimal. But in their defense, advertising, linens, lotions, tables, appointments, set ups—everything is there. Walk in, work, and leave.

The rooms were too cold in my opinion and the clients had to be covered with layers of sheets and blankets with heating pads under them. I asked if the room temperature could be raised a few degrees, to seventy, but was denied by popular demand. The other therapists would get too hot while working. I had many repeat clients, so I was busy. But it was exhausting to work that mechanically.

You came in on the days you worked and picked a room for the day. I selected my room the first day I got there. I had walked into each room and felt the air. I selected that room and would get in early to turn on the table heat to help warm up the room.

I had that one for a week until someone came in before me and claimed it. I thought it was odd because I was generally there before anyone else. I had to select another room. When I did, someone claimed that one too. There was a smoothie bar next door, and we could hear the blenders cranking out smoothies through the wall. Someone claimed that room too. When I asked two other therapists why they always took the room I chose, they said I left good energy in a room after I worked there all day.

Then I was asked to work with a young male therapist to do a couples' massage. The protocol was after the massage, we retreated into a break room until the clients left. The young man followed me into the break room and closed the door behind us, then leaned against the door to block anyone from entering so we were alone. Then he proceeded to tell me, "You work too hard. We don't get paid enough to work as hard as you do, and you make the rest of us look bad!"

I was stunned. Totally shocked! I looked directly at him.

"It's what I do, and I can't short anybody without giving them my best. And you are right, I don't get paid enough, but I'm here for the time being, and I will continue to do my best."

I kept the conversation to myself, but I couldn't help but notice a change in everyone. I kept to myself after that. They didn't team build, which was becoming uncomfortable.

A few days later, the owner asked if I would work on a friend of his. He was at the fitness center in the plaza and this guy was a place kicker for a minor team. I agreed because he knew I was into sports massage and he was sending clients my way. He recommended that player see me, and I agreed, thinking it could lead to something more.

The player said he liked my work very much and would be seeing me again, but I didn't receive a tip from him. When you work for a business, you hope for gratuity. I envisioned working on someone in the minors could lead to working with a whole team . . . minor, or major? The thoughts ran through my head. Was I capable of working with these players' hard bodies? I would have to keep my own good body mechanics to protect myself, but it could have led to recognition and better pay.

The owner asked me the next day if the kicker he recommended tipped me well.

"Maybe he didn't like me? I didn't receive a tip. At least, if he did, I didn't get it."

He was leaning back in his chair with his feet up on his desk. Then he sat up and began dialing his phone to call him, and as I left, I heard him say, "You didn't tip MY GIRL?" I stepped out of the office and thought that was embarrassing.

Maybe he didn't like my massage after all, I thought. Either way, it was time for me to move on. The thought of being "his girl"? Not my cup of tea.

The next day, the owner was waiting for me to come in and handed me a twenty-dollar bill, and I told him thank you but I would be leaving at the end of the week. He asked me to step into his office to talk about it.

"I'm driving fifty-two miles each day to get to and from here, and with traffic, it takes me an hour each way. And I don't feel this is a good fit for me. The concept is good, but I really want something different for myself."

He thanked me and said if I ever changed my mind, there would be a place for me there.

I haven't been back.

Chapter 23
It's What I Do Most!

Myoskeletal Alignment/Techniques, Created by Erik Dalton —Freedom from Pain Institute

Neck-sciatic and shoulder pain are the most common issues I hear from my clients.

Whether they are corporate people, sports related, or injuries—repetitive or accident—or all of the above. This is what we massage therapists do!

I was one of the first people to sign up for this class, I was told at sign-in. I had signed up six months in advance. I wasn't going to miss it!

What I didn't expect was a week before this seminar, I had to have an hysterectomy. At the advice of my doctor, it should not be delayed. I wasn't allowed to work, drive, or carry anything for six weeks, so my husband had to drive me. I had a hotel room for the three-day seminar already paid for and wasn't going to miss it. I couldn't participate in everything, but I was there in body, mind, and spirit. I approached Mr. Dalton to let him know of my situation, and he wanted me up front to keep an eye on me. There were about fifty people in attendance, and that meant twenty-five tables were set up in a large room with speakers, video cameras, and screens, so everything was visible.

Another massage-therapist friend of mine, who had also signed up for this class, partnered with me during the three days. I was thankful for her too. She helped me get through it. We also partnered with someone next to us if I couldn't participate in something. There were quite a few chiropractors or chiropractic students in this class also. But it was exhausting for me. Erik Dalton came to me afterward and said he was proud of me. It brought tears to my eyes to hear him say that. My mentor!

It is always exciting for me to watch and learn and practice new techniques—his books are my study guides.

"Myoskeletal Alignment" sounds technical and complicated to add to a business card. So I changed it to what people look for most: "Pain Management."

Chapter 24
Finding My Niche?

Salon, Day Spa, or Chiropractor?

Why not all three?

Where was my mind? I was looking for something but wasn't sure what and that seemed to be the answer.

I received two messages on the same day about places looking for a massage therapist, so I interviewed at both. They thought they were interviewing me, but I was interviewing them as well.

Dr. E. was relaxed and casual as I sat in front of him, and we talked about me coming into the two offices owned by him and his brother. I could work two or three days a week in one office and two days in the other office. I was being cautious about agreeing to work with them at all since the last chiro I worked at was not a pleasant experience. I felt skeptical. And he did too, as his office had a not-so-good experience with a therapist before me. We decided to give it a two-week trial before we signed any contracts. I wasn't sure we would be a good meld.

Then I had another interview to go to at a salon and day spa, which also sounded enticing but wasn't exactly what I was looking for.

My personal preference was the clinical or healthful type of massage, which would be found at a chiropractor office, but could I work with those two brothers at the chiropractic office?

There were two offices, and I lived between them. One was seventeen miles from my house, and super busy with clientele in the midst of shopping, schools, and offices. The other was less than five miles, and the clientele was a bit more relaxed. That would be interesting. Also the offices were in neighboring counties.

Now, the salon and day spa was busy with six hairdressers, an aesthetician, manicure/pedicurist, and also close to where I lived. So, I had a dilemma and had to choose.

So, I chose to do both. Work at the chiropractor office during the week—alternating two days at one office and two days at the other—and work the salon on Friday and Saturday.

After all, this was going to be a trial with all of us!

That gave me the best of three worlds. Each office had its interesting points. I remained an independent and took care of my own laundry, lotions, and taxes. They had the massage tables. We each came to an agreement of terms. My one requirement—if you want to call it that—was:

"We agree to disagree. If I work with you, we are going to disagree on things as we go along and that is okay, as long as we agree to disagree and not have conflict. Rather, we talk it out or work it out between us." I received blank stares when I said that, but I needed to be clear before there was any uncertainty.

That felt good for me. The chiropractors had another therapist also, but we never had a chance to work together, and several came and went during my stay there. I really liked working with the people in the office, not just the doctors but the staff too. I didn't want to turn down either of them or really put myself out there by agreeing to such. I worked six days a week. A couple of days were only half days at the office, and I was able to select what hours I wanted to work and give myself some time off as needed. Being in the chiropractors' office was helpful for me to learn more of the clinical aspect of massage. The salon kept me balanced, being with the girls on Friday and Saturday.

I remained an independent between all the offices, which meant I was not contracted to any one place. I could work wherever. I quit doing house calls, although I was asked occasionally and sometimes would for a special occasion. But it was above and beyond the call of duty.

They all knew about the other. They each had specific hours. I had clients from the spa come see me at the office. If they needed specific work and their insurance covered it, they would come to the office. If I had clients at the office who needed to see me after hours, or on Saturday, they could come to the spa. It all balanced out.

I had a couple of clients who would contact me on the fly, asking where I was and when I was available and would come to either the office or the salon. It was great advertising for both. I liked the idea of knowing the chiropractors to refer them if I thought it necessary. They recommended clients to me. For some clients, it was convenient either way.

People always seemed to be more comfortable going to a medical type of office and not just a massage establishment. I felt more respected too—and not like just a massage therapist earning a dollar. Being with the chiropractors, we could talk anatomy and medical terms. That helped patients and clientele understand I was serious about my profession. The salon clientele who knew I also worked with the chiropractors felt more comfortable with me. I did more of a clinical and medical type of massage.

We all settled into a routine that lasted ten years!

Belgian Lady, Very Little English

At the chiropractors' office, an elderly lady visiting from Belgium was brought in by her grandson. He made her an appointment for a massage as she had requested. The grandson was unsure about taking her just anywhere, so he brought her to the chiropractors' office. He had heard of me being a mature woman and felt confident enough with that to leave his grandmother in my hands for her first massage.

The day he brought her in, I met with them at the reception desk and shook their hands. He was quite tall at about six-foot-four, and she was lucky to be five feet tall and was very frail. She spoke very little English and didn't weigh a hundred pounds. So, I asked him to come back to the room with us so he could see the massage room where I did my massages and so he knew she would be safe with me. And to interpret that she would need to take off her dress, lie down on the table faceup, and cover herself with a sheet. We left her in the room and stepped outside in the hall where I told him to be back in an hour and she would be ready. I would do my best to make her happy and make it a good experience for her.

I gave her a few minutes as I went to the bathroom and washed my hands again then came back to knock on the door and peeped in to make sure she was ready for me.

She was lying on the massage table with the sheet over her, tightly clutched in her hands under her chin.

Instead of me standing over her, I brought my stool around to the side of the table and sat down on her right side. I needed to earn her trust and put her at ease. I reached for her right hand and gently pulled it to me to massage. She began to relax as I spoke to her, asking for her hand and welcoming her, thanking her for coming to see me. I was glad to have met her and hoped her visit would be good. She didn't understand everything, but she began to be at ease.

I knew she had removed her dress as I saw it lying on the chair but she had left everything else on. The little woman had on a bra, a camisole, a full slip, a half-slip, panty hose, and compression stockings over her panty hose, which made it very difficult to give her a real, full body massage. I almost laughed out loud. It was so cute, but I made it happen.

After her hands and arms, I massaged her shoulders and neck. She began to melt onto the table. She loved her feet rubbed even through the stockings. I did reflexology and that was when she started talking about how she loved being in America. How when she was a little girl, the Americans came into her town and saved them from the Germans, and she was grateful to the American soldiers in their big machines and tanks. They waved flags as soldiers past by and one soldier gave her chocolate to eat.

What? This lady spoke English quite well!

She told of the American cemetery near her town that was very big and so sad to see.

"Very pretty," she said in her accent, with tears in her eyes. "So sad to see. You should come see." She turned over to her tummy, still covered by a sheet, and I massaged her back as best I could through the layers of clothes she still had on. It may have been too traumatic for her to take off anything more.

I always ask folks to get out of clothes to their comfort level. Most take off everything and leave on the skivvies or underwear. Some take it all off. Some people go commando! But everyone is always covered or draped while on the massage table.

I was so moved that she was so comfortable with me. She bubbled over with excitement about how the Americans saved them back in World War II.

I was holding her arm, and she was chatting in English as we walked back slowly down the hall to the reception area. Her grandson was surprised to see her so chatty. She had a big smile on her face and wanted to pay me as she started to open her purse, but her grandson had already taken care of the payment, then she wanted to tip, but I said no. Her grandson told her everything was taken care of in her native language.

She gave me a long, genuine hug and, with tears in both of our eyes, everyone was left wondering what went on in the massage room. I told her she could come back and see me, but the grandson said she was going to be leaving to go back to Belgium soon. I probably would not see her again. She taught me a little bit of history that I had forgotten.

That was special meeting her.

Sandy

She came to see me for her first massage at the recommendation of the chiropractor. She was in her seventies, worked part-time as a receptionist at a doctor's office, and was also a caregiver to her ninety-something-year-old mother. She was not quite five feet tall, not thin but not heavy, and always tried to smile even when in pain. She always had on a full face of makeup, her hair always done, and she was always nicely dressed.

She let me massage her that first time and I could tell she was going to be aching after that massage. Just detoxing her alone was going to make her sore, and I cautioned her to drink a lot of water afterward to help lessen her soreness.

About six months later, she came to see me again. She told me she was really sore after her first massage but about three days later, she felt really, really good. She started seeing me once every three or four months. I could tell she was in constant pain and tried to hide it. During one of her massages, I asked her to please give me a chance and see me at least once a month for a tune-up before she started to hurt so much. The massages were painful but in a good way. Otherwise she was in constant pain all over in a not-so-good way. So, she agreed.

"I will see you in a month," she said.

She came to see me once a month for three months. After her third massage, three months later, she sat up on the massage table just before I left the room, and with a big, bright-red smile said, "I actually enjoyed that massage! It practically didn't hurt at all!"

She was booked for a tune-up massage each month from then on. I saw her every four weeks regularly after that. She came in with a smile, which told me her body knew it was about time, and left with a bigger smile, until her mom passed away. She then decided to retire, and driving nearly an hour just to see me became a struggle, so I helped her find another therapist closer to where she lived.

Massage gave her a new lease on life, she told me, and her smiles were genuine.

Last I heard, she was taking a two-week Mediterranean cruise with a group of lady friends!

Migraines

People with migraines, I have empathy for you. I have suffered from them myself during certain times in my life.

I have several, regular clients who suffer with them and will call if they think I can help. Sometimes I can, and sometimes I cannot. Most feel better or at least they feel I'm trying and that trying is better than nothing.

One such client called me at seven a.m. on a Sunday morning, pleading for me to help him.

"I've been awake since five a.m. with a migraine, Lynn. I waited until seven to call you. Can I come see you, please? I can't drive, but my wife will bring me."

"I don't have a key to the office to meet you. How did you find me?"

"That's okay, I'll come to your house. I looked you up through the internet. Lynn, please. If you won't, I'll find someone else."

"Okay, okay. I'll give you my address," I told him.

He had been in the office several times for me, or the chiropractor, or both, to ease his painful migraines as well as seeing other specialists and doctors. But that morning, I was the one he called for help. He was there within the hour; his wife drove him and dropped him off at my home office door and then left with the kids to come back an hour later to pick him up.

The next morning, he was in the chiropractors' office to see Dr. E., telling him how I helped him with his migraine the day before at my house, which didn't sit too well with Dr. E. I didn't arrive at the office until late morning and debated with myself if I should tell him about my early

Sunday morning visitor. Shortly after I arrived, he asked me to come into his office.

"You cannot take patients out of the office," he said, not angry but stern.

"I know . . . but when someone calls me at seven a.m. on a Sunday morning, asking and then telling me if I didn't see him, he would go somewhere else, I did what you would have done. I don't have a key to the office nor do I want one or want to drive all the way here."

We grinned at each other as we both knew it was a stalemate. Agree to disagree!

"I know you know I have a massage table at my house. And I know you have an adjustment table at your house for those little . . . whatever situations you do at your house." He tried to hide his grin.

"I did us a favor to keep a patient happy. He won't be seeing me at my house after this, I assure you. His insurance takes care of him here in the office, so that won't be an issue. Desperate people take desperate measures when they are in pain. What else could I do?"

We never spoke of it again. But it cleared the air.

A month later the man's wife came to see me at the office with a migraine. I could tell by the look on her face that she was miserable.

"What have you been doing to yourself?" I asked as she was lying down.

"I don't know, but I hope you can help me. It's been four days."

"Oh my, why did you wait so long?"

"I didn't want to be a bother since I don't work."

"But you do work! You have a lot of responsibility working at home with a big house, a husband, and kids."

She was laying faceup, and I sat at her head to bring my

hands up under her shoulders and under her neck, up to the base of her skull.

Hmmm, I thought. I gently massaged around her head and scalp feeling for anything obvious, and I found it!

I did the same movement several times to help unblock her lymph channels, or interstitial fluids under the skin of her scalp. Then I stopped with my hands under her head and my fingertips under her occiput, holding her steady.

"How are you feeling now?" I asked.

"Oh my, it feels like the headache is draining out of my head," she said.

"Literally, it is!" I confirmed to her. I felt a bubble around her skull on the right side of her scalp. My fingers were at the base of her skull and it actually felt like water was running through my fingertips. It was all happening under her skin, yet I could feel it. How incredible that was for me! I continued the massage for the remainder of the allotted time, and she looked so different than when she came in.

She was smiling and had a hug for me too!

I feel so blessed when things like that happen because of my touch sensibility.

Sensitivity vs. Sensibility

Sensitivity is the quality of being sensitive!
Sensibility is the ability to sense, feel, or perceive,
Especially to be sensitive to the feelings of others.

Bert!

A longtime, occasional client—Bert—came to see me with lower back, and sometimes neck, pain during the fall and winter. He was in his early eighties, and at that particular time, he could hardly drive or walk with the excruciating back pain he experienced. It took almost an hour for him to drive to see me, but that visit was the most severe.

When he drove up, I met him in the driveway to help him in. It was difficult for him to walk, and he was slightly bent over and unable to stand up straight. One of the worst times I had ever seen him.

I had to help him into the room and took off his shoes and socks for him, as he couldn't bend over. He was constantly moaning and writhing in pain. I left the room for him to finish getting undressed in private, but he didn't care. When you are in a lot of pain, you don't care who sees what.

I had the table warmer on to help him relax after he got onto the table. I had a pillow at his knees to take the pressure off his lower back when he laid down. Once he got situated and covered with the top sheet, I came in to begin his massage.

He tried to relax as I began massaging and talking to him. I asked how he had gotten in such a bad shape but he said he didn't know. He just insisted he hadn't done anything to cause his severe back pain. It just came on and he was hoping for relief. Bert liked to play Santa Claus during Christmas season. He had a long, white beard—not so long during the summer, but in September he'd let it grow a bit more and got it whitened before Christmas season. He fit the part very well, physically, and his wife too.

I did my usual massage and stretches as best I could do on a man of his age, but nothing seemed to release his pain.

"Bert," I said, "what have you been doing the past few weeks?" Maybe it was something different I didn't know about?

He had done some traveling to visit his son and daughter-in-law in another state and got back not too long ago.

He began to get a little teary-eyed and emotional.

"I'm sorry," he said. "That's not very masculine of me to show emotion."

"This is a massage room, and emotions bubble up without warning here! The good thing is, it stays here. No one need know. I feel something else is really going on here, and I don't know what it is. I've never seen you this bad before."

He was beginning to relax, and the little bit of tears helped. I massaged his limbs and stretched his legs. He was not a real active person and had a bit of atrophy. Stretching him was difficult.

"Okay, Bert. What has you tied up in knots? What HAVE you been doing? How is your son?"

"Well?" he began. "You mean like me sitting at my son's death bed holding his hand with his wife for three days?"

"You and your daughter-in-law have been sitting on both sides of your sons' death bed with a circle of hands praying for three solid days and he what? Just woke up?"

"YES!" he said, looking up at me.

I was dumbfounded. This man and his wife were devout members of their church and were deeply into their religious studies. They prayed with many people to help them through illnesses and hard times. I didn't ask any more questions, but I knew he hadn't connected what was causing his current pain.

"Well, Bert, there's your answer!"

"Answer to what?"

"You have taken on your son's pain. I don't know what his problem was, but holding onto his hand, as a father, you've taken away your son's pain, and it has now manifested itself in you at your weakest point—your back!

"I don't know how to explain it but when you held his hand in a circle of prayer, his pain was distributed to you, and maybe her, because you accepted it. I know this sounds crazy, but you are a religious man, and you know Pieta! That's incredible. Now, you need to let it go, and I think I can help."

I continued to massage this man in the state he was in.

"Open your heart and be joyful for what you have done." I was saying silent prayers at this point. He was compressed, and I needed to decompress him as well as I could. Now that he realized what it could have been and accepted what he had done, he could let it go.

When I finished, he felt better but needed some time to detox. He dressed slowly because he was still in pain and trying to digest what I had said.

Three days later, he left a message on my phone.

"Lynn, this is Bert! You don't need to call me back, but I just wanted to let you know I feel great! And I think you hit the nail on the head. You have helped me in the past many times but not to this degree. And I want to thank you again!"

I have massaged Santa Claus. Can I add that to my business card?

Chapter 25
Opening a New Door!

Craniosacral Therapy

A massage therapist friend called me to tell me there was an introductory class for craniosacral therapy being presented in Atlanta and asked if I wanted to go with her. I had heard of it but didn't really know what it was about. It really didn't sound like my thing. I mean *cranial* and *sacral*? We massaged the back all the time, that's what people love! But she told me that it took a special skill to do that work, and we were seasoned and she thought I would really like to learn about this. Besides, it was an introductory class to engage the right people for the techniques. It was not for everybody.

That intro was on a Saturday class to listen, talk, and experience that unique massage modality that most people don't comprehend. I was willing to at least open this new door and judge for myself if it might be something I wanted to pursue.

We met and drove together to the first intro class. There were about forty people that Saturday. Some from as far away as the Northeast and Pennsylvania area.

We did some exercises to help us feel the concept, like balancing nickels on our fingertips to feel the weight of them then two people held blown-up balloons with their fingertips—two hands on top and two hands on the sides, squeezing the balloon with fingertips and using no more pressure than the weight of a nickel to feel the delicate compression of the balloon.

The challenges of a massage therapist are to feel muscles then isolate them to work out the knots and kinks, but now we were feeling for fluid flow within the tissues. I won't get into detail, but I was VERY intrigued, and having a friend to learn with made a big difference too. We were able to study and practice together.

That new door was wide open. That introductory class was the beginning of a commitment for what became five classes over a period of two years.

During the lunch break of that first intro class, a few had already dropped out.

In September, at the Level I of our first three-day seminar, we were down to about twenty-five people. In February at the Level II, and in August at the Level III, we lost a few more people, and by April for the Level IV—which was four days of classes and our last set—we had twelve people who saw it through. For me, I was excited for the next class and the next, as were the other eleven who chose to continue. Those last four days were very intense. It took place in the North Georgia Mountains at a retreat. It included watching a video of the embryo and how human life begins.

One afternoon, it rained and we sat on rocking chairs on a second-story wooden porch, facing the woods as if we were in the treetops. The rain came straight down, no wind at all, as we sat perfectly still in meditation, watching and listening to the raindrops hit the leaves. Sitting so still and quiet long enough that squirrels ran around us as the rain came down.

The next day, we went horseback riding during the afternoon through the woods to feel connected with the horse under us and at nature surrounding us.

We laid in the sun, on the grass, to feel the earth beneath us. We practiced and recapped everything we learned and studied in the previous two years. Even shared some of our experiences and connected the pieces between man and God in meditation, discussion, and prayer.

We split the final twelve into two groups, and each person took a turn on the table with five people touching them. One pair of hands for each leg, arm, and head to experience the rebirth process. Then we talked about our experience afterward. INTENSE!

Now there was a Level V, but both my friend and I declined on that one as it was six days of recap and a test to be certified.

These are the adventures of being a massage therapist if you are really into it!

Those two years honed a new skill of touch in me. Hence "hands-on gift"!

I felt it was already being honed, but now I understood.

Craniosacral therapy added to my business card!

Chapter 26
Another Door to Open!

Swe-Thai and Thai Foot

Thai massage had been in the back of my mind for years. I had purchased a book about it years ago and tried to study it, but it isn't the same as having someone to learn from. I was intrigued by it and thought someday I would find the right person to learn from and take a class.

Well, in the spring of 2016, I received an invite to a Swe-Thai and Thai foot massage seminar. Not really what I wanted but my time was running out for this. I needed to get my CEUs for my license renewal, and at least I would get a taste of real Thai massage. It was early in the year, and it would give me an opportunity to qualify for my renewal and not wait until the last minute.

It was two classes, three days each, a month apart. The first class was the Swe-Thai, which was a combination of Swedish massage and Thai massage. That was in March. The concept was interesting as some of the techniques meant the therapist would have to sometimes stand or kneel on the table with the client.

During that class, the instructor also announced she was going to Thailand that fall and asked if anyone wanted to sign up to go learn real Thai massage in Thailand.

BINGO! Oh, I wish! That would be a dream trip! I thought.

But for now, I need to focus on three days of classes. I had a hotel room for two nights so I wouldn't have to drive each day. Each day of class began at eight a.m., and I would look over the instructor's literature, pictures, and items from Thailand. She herself learned Thai massage in Thailand and practiced for many years. This would be her fifteenth trip of accompanying people for classes.

By the second day, when I called my husband to check in, I mentioned to him she was offering trips to Thailand to learn their ways of massage, but we both shrugged it off as a pipe dream.

We had already decided we would save money to spend Christmas with our son Elton, who lived in Hawaii. Well now, what if I went to Thailand instead? Hawaii would have to be next year. After the third day of class, I made my decision to go. I drove home that evening after the third day of the seminar and announced I was going to Thailand.

"Are you serious?" asked Ernie.

"Yes! I am going to Thailand to learn Thai massage. I've always wanted to learn Thai massage since I graduated from massage therapy school and kept putting it off because of other things, and now, for my sixty-fifth birthday in October, I'm going. Do you want to go with me? This will be my last, big hoopla because I don't know how much longer I will be able to work. I will be able to write my trip off as training."

"No! How long is it going to be for?" he asked.

"I'll be gone for nineteen days. I have until September to pay for it. And you can either go to Hawaii to stay with

Elton, and I'll meet you on the way back, or stay here. We won't be able to spend Christmas in Hawaii though. We can't afford both trips."

"If I go, do you think we could go to Vietnam while we are that close?" he asked.

"I doubt that very much. The closest we'll get to Vietnam is flying over it."

This was a big decision for me. I must be out of my mind. It was halfway around the world! We kept looking at the world globe and realized how far away Thailand was. That was going to be a long flight. A day to get there, and we would fly across the International Date Line.

We've been to Amsterdam, England to visit our son and family, and the Dominican Republic for a vacation, but this is a huge step for us.

I called our son in Hawaii to clue him in on the situation and get his reaction. He liked to travel too and is a rock guitar player who has met quite a few rock musicians. He always talked about Japan and wanting to visit there. Living in Hawaii, working as a bartender, he met a lot of people from all over the world. He was ecstatic.

"Gosh, Mom. Can Dad live without you for nineteen days?"

"Well, I thought I would send him to you to hang out with, and I'll meet up with you later on my way back. We are in the planning stage. We'll see what shakes out. Just wanted to run it by you."

By the next month, when I attended the Thai foot massage class, a few others had decided to go as well, and when I asked how many were going so far, she had about twelve who were interested and gave me much more information. So, when I got back home to tell Ernie, he decided he would go too, as an extra.

About a month later, nearing June, I asked about Elton since I thought it would be nice if he could also come as an extra. It would be a slow time for his activities as well. He had his passport updated, and since he was out there in the Pacific Ocean, it sounded so close to Thailand at the time. Since we wouldn't be having Christmas together with him in Hawaii, we made arrangements for him to join us for our last days in Thailand.

He could only come for the last ten days, but it would give him and his dad a chance to hang together while I was attending classes. Then we could also see some sites together and share the experience with him.

Sounds like a Good Plan

As the time grew closer, the excitement did too! We were briefed on the dos and don'ts of a foreign country. The instructor sent us a package of literature and pamphlets about some of the sightseeing adventures we would be doing and not just for classes. I tried to study a little of the Thai language, but it was hard. Our coordinator made us feel relaxed and confident about the whole trip.

She also coordinated Elton's trip from Hawaii for him too.

The group of twenty-two met at the airport for the first time. Several had flown in from other places to meet in Atlanta. We all flew out of Atlanta a few days after Halloween, and our first stop was Seoul, South Korea! We switched planes and then went on to Chang Mai, Thailand. Approximately twenty-two-total hours of flying.

Chapter 27
Chang Mai

We were very tired and just wanted to go to bed when we arrived at the airport. We were loaded into a couple of vans and driven to a restaurant and treated to a meal upon arrival. It was midnight there, when we ate our first Thai dinner. The restaurant was next to a river, and we were seated outside looking across the river in moonlight. It was pleasantly warm and tropical. Most of us were too tired to eat much. We had flown across the International Date Line which meant it was noon back home, yesterday.

We enjoyed being outside after the long trip, and it felt good to have a light breeze against our faces. After the meal, we again loaded up in the vans and were taken to the hotel that would be home for the next nineteen days.

Ahh, a nice room and bed, a shower and sleep. We were on the other side of the world. Who would have ever thought? I was glad Ernie had come with me to share the experience together.

A few hours of sleep and stretching out made a world of difference, and we assembled in the lobby for a breakfast, Thailand style—a continental Thai breakfast, you could say. We had dry cereals with milk, cooked eggs and sausage that resembled the Vienna sausages from a can, little pancakes with syrup, always rice and chicken soup dishes in spicy hot sauces, along with fresh juices, fruits, and melon. The coffee was really good, as I understood they grew coffee locally.

After breakfast, we assembled for a guided walking tour with our coordinator. We were half a mile from the main area, money exchanges, restaurants, and Tai Pei Gate, the old city. It was hundreds of years old and some of the original, mile-long square's wall still stood as well as the moat. A mix of old and new with several well-known franchises from the States.

Always carry a business card from the hotel with you in case you got lost. Then you could always flag down a tuktuk, and they would get you back to the hotel.

> A tuk-tuk is a motorcycle with a wide seat on the back that can hold up to three people. Most of them have a canopy over the seats for protection from sun and rain. A motorized rickshaw!

The next day, we loaded into the vans and were driven to the Chang Mai Blind Institute. We were ushered in and led into a room with a long row of small, thin cushions on the floor to accommodate all of us. No one had to undress, as massages were done with clothes on and without lotions or oils. After we laid down, the blind therapists came in, feeling their way to us and began massaging. We were treated to a massage all at the same time in same place. The timing was good after such a long trip. We were still feeling jet-lagged and were getting acclimated to our new time. Classes were going to begin in a couple more days.

The excitement was building. And calling a hotel room "home" was different. We went out that first day and changed three hundred US dollars to baht, Thailand's currency. I hadn't heard of it before until I signed up for the class. I thought it would be easy to remember, but it took me some time to wrap my mind around the strange currency. Three hundred dollars equated to about fifteen thousand baht. We laid all that out on the bed to take a picture of it and feel rich.

During the course of our stay, some people in our group saw dentists and doctors while we were there. Tailored clothing stores were plentiful. You could walk into a shop, pick out fabric for a shirt, outfit, or dress, be measured for anything, and try it on the next day.

Seemed like everyone knew how to sew and massage. It was a part of their culture.

The first week of Thai massage classes began on the Monday after we arrived in Chang Mai. I got up, showered, and was down for breakfast by seven a.m. Then went back to the room for a bit of quiet before assembling in the lobby to wait for the truck at 8:15 a.m.

If you missed the truck, you had to find your own way to class. I wouldn't miss it because I would have gotten lost trying to find the school. We had two pickup trucks with bench seats on both sides of truck bed and a canopy to protect us from the sun, wind, or rain. The fumes were bad. Most of us would cover our noses and mouths with cloths to protect us from all the vehicle fumes. It was a common practice with most of the locals too.

Our twenty-minute commute became an adventure too as we rode along their main highway, which was similar to our interstate.

When we arrived at the school, we had to take off our shoes and walk in barefoot. We had a small, flat, rectangle basket with our names on it that would have our freshly cleaned clothes to wear for the day. Women and men were directed to different rooms to change into these scrub-type clothes. We kept the basket and any personal items we brought in a small, cube locker. At the end of the day, we changed back into our clothes and turned in the basket with the scrubs to be cleaned again for the next day.

All classes begin with a chant or type of prayer. Then we each were given warm washcloths to wash our feet. Anytime we left the building or took a break for lunch, we had to wash our feet before we began the second half of the day. As long as we were in the building, we were barefoot.

> I'm glad I had gotten a pedicure before we left the States. I also had gotten a pedicure while there at a local establishment.

Each day we had fifteen-minute breaks in the morning and the afternoon for bathroom and tea. Hot tea was always available and encouraged to drink on break with small, fresh bananas. Those bananas were the sweetest I had ever tasted, and it was fresh off the tree. For lunch, we had forty-five minutes to go out, if desired. I went out for lunch the first day to an open-air market that was across the street from the school. Crossing that street, I felt like a duck in a shooting gallery. There were six lanes of highway.

The outdoor market was an experience in itself. Raw fish, fried worms, crickets, and fruits. It was all eye-opening. I wasn't too hungry after the sights and smells of all that was offered.

As I was leaving to go back across the street, I spied an older lady stirring a pot of oil and asked, "Tofu?" and the lady nodded. The young girl was wrapping several pieces of fried tofu and a small sausage patty in a folded paper together, and I asked for one, which she smiled and handed to me. I gave her a coin that looked like a quarter, and she tried to give me back change that looked like a nickel, but I told her to keep it. She looked at me with wide eyes and looked at the older lady who nodded then looked back at me and smiled.

The second day at lunch, I went with several others to a store that was about a quarter-mile walk from the school. It was similar to our large variety store, and the food court there was good and busy. I ate too much and was miserable. After that, I opted to stay at the school and have tea and a protein bar. I couldn't eat a big lunch and crawl on the floor during class, so I opted to eat light.

I ate breakfast at the hotel in the morning, tea and a banana for breaks, and tea and a protein bar for lunch. After we got back to the hotel at night, Ernie and I would stay at the hotel for dinner since, by then, I was exhausted from having class all day. My stamina built up, and after Elton joined us, we would go out somewhere different. Our favorite restaurant ended up being a tiny Italian place next to couple of American fast-food franchises. Massage surely opened doors for me!

Numerous times I thought about the years I'd been doing massage and how I learned new modalities every year. When I graduated massage school, I researched for my massage table to have a table that would accommodate Thai massage by being flat on the floor. Someday I would learn about Thai massage. Someday was then, but . . .

All training was on the floor and difficult for us Westerners who have been sitting on chairs most of our lives. They don't use a lot of chairs, therefore keeping their flexibility as they age, and we Westerners become atrophied starting at a young age by sitting on chairs.

I was impressed with all our teachers at the school. They saw people from all over the world and spoke English very well. They were in their thirties, forties, and fifties. The class just ahead of us was from England, and all the students were very young, maybe in their twenties. They graduated a week before we did. The school also had other classes in another area that we did not see, but we knew the students in those classes were there taking advance classes in Thai massage.

Our classes were usually eight to a classroom with one instructor. Each classroom had four mats on the floor with two people per mat. My instructor would walk into the room, pass out a clean sheet for each mat, then a washcloth for each of us to wash our feet with, then squat down on the floor, flat-footed like a toddler, with no effort whatsoever. How could she do that? And me? I was sixty-five years old and wished I could have done that twenty years ago. I would have more flexibility back then. I didn't quit though. I knew they separated us older and slower people, which I was thankful for. I wouldn't want to hold up the younger and faster learners. A few in our class even signed up for advance classes later on for another trip.

If I ever go back to Chang Mai, it would be for a visit not for vocation.

I highly recommend everyone experience the old city of Siam, now Chang Mai.

Between classes and during weekends, we toured orchid farms, the elephant sanctuaries, rode oxcarts and elephants, and cruised the river on an open raft.

Elton met up with us for the last ten days, and it was great sharing the experience with him. While I was in class during the day, he and his dad would explore the old city and get foot or body massages every day. Elton even had a shirt made to fit. We watched him get measured, and he picked out a fabric and style and was back the next day to try it on. It was unbelievable how that shirt fit.

We visited the jade factory—yes, real jade—and they educated us on the art of jade jewelry and the carving of real jade. We learned that there were different grades of jade. We also visited the umbrella factory and the silk factory. Oh, I love silk. I brought back silk scarves for friends and some of my clients, and jade earrings to all the gals I worked with at the salon and the chiro offices, as well as a few special purchases for myself.

Temples!

Temples, temples, and more temples! Everywhere we looked there were temples covered with gold. Or covered with glass or tiny mirrors or white and ivory. Some of them were old, and I mean centuries old, and a few of them were new. There were small ones. Like a one-car garage, or medium like a small house, and there were ones that were grandiose!

One of my classmates wanted to take a walkabout toward the end of our stay to take pictures of temples within walking distance of our hotel. She asked me to come along and I did. She had a map of several temples and set out to seek and investigate them. She loved photography and had brought an expensive camera with her.

We were approaching one small temple, about the size of a one-car garage, in an out-of-the-way area. At no time did we feel unsafe. It was early afternoon, and as we stood in front of this small temple, we talked about going in. It was all lavish and decked out in tile and mirrors. There were four large steps up to the opening and in through the doorway and a short hall, I could see the Buddha inside and stain-glass windows.

"I can see all I want to see from here," I said. "If you want to go in, I'll wait here. And I'm sure we have to take off our shoes to enter." We stood there pondering and peering into the small place when out of nowhere, this monk appeared next to us.

"You must take off shoes before entering temple," he said, startling us, and we jumped. I looked right at him, in the eyes. He was a handsome young man, shorter than me, in his orange monk garb. Then I looked down and away.

"Yes, of course! We will," we both said. As we looked down at our shoes and back at the temple steps, then back to him. He had disappeared!

"Where did he go?" we both asked in unison, looking up and down the area around. We even looked at the ground to see if there was a manhole or something for him to appear from.

"That's creepy. And I looked right at him too," I said.

"We are not supposed to look them in the eyes," she reminded me, as she was removing her shoes to go into the temple.

"Yes, I remembered, but I couldn't help it. He appeared right beside me out of nowhere, startling me and disappeared the same way." I walked back and forth in front of the temple to look at both sides. Where did he go?

"And this temple isn't large enough for him to hide in the walls. We would have seen him walk that way! They walk barefoot and this terrain is a little rocky. He didn't make a sound." I was speaking to her as she walked inside and took pictures. I walked around out front, looking for any sign of the mysterious, disappearing monk. She came out and put her shoes back on and we continued walking past that temple to the next one a block away, still not seeing anyone. Where did he go?

We walked a few more blocks, and I decided I had seen enough temples for one day and headed back through the old city, stopping at a few shops for souvenirs before returning back to the hotel.

Our last two days of school came, and we learned how to transition some of what we had learned on the floor to a massage table. It was much easier for some of us to stand than to be on our hands and knees. Although we still needed to use our hands and legs to do some of the techniques we had learned. I had older clients who wouldn't have been able to get up off the floor should they get down.

We had a graduation ceremony and certificates were handed out and photos taken.

Wow, it was almost over.

Things We Shared

My husband, Ernie, had a great time meeting people while I was working away in the classroom. He met the owners or managers of restaurants he liked and frequented. He also got massages every other day. He, Elton, and I went and got foot massages at a place my husband was partial to. We went in and had our feet washed and were ushered into another room with large, white-leather recliners. They gave us tea and wafers too. I ate the tea and wafers . . . they fell asleep.

One time when we were together, a tuktuk driver who didn't speak English, but I remember a big smile on his face as he touched Elton's arm and made a gesture of playing a guitar. Then he tugged at his own hair indicating Elton's long hair. He nodded back at the driver with a "yes." I thought the driver was going to ask for his autograph, but he didn't.

Everywhere Elton went, he was asked if he was a rocker because of his long hair.

He walked around late one evening to check out some of the small, local bars. While at a small bar, he had gotten into a conversation with a guy from Spain, who spoke English and Spanish. A few minutes later, he went to the other end of the bar to meet another guy who was from Brazil and didn't speak English, and they used their phones to translate. Then Elton thought the Spain fellow would be able to translate, as his Spanish was similar to Portuguese. When he asked the guy, he said sure he could try to translate. A woman sitting at a table nearby overheard that conversation and spoke up saying she was from Australia but spoke Portuguese, and could she be of help.

"That's even better," Elton said. "We all need to talk!"

And friendships were born. They all exchanged numbers and became social media friends. They agreed to meet again before they all parted from Chang Mai. They did get together twice more before we left.

Several nights during our stay in the hotel, there would be karaoke. The local patrons loved their karaoke. It was amusing hearing them singing in their native language. Even stranger was hearing them sing English songs not knowing what they were singing. Our son sang a few songs for us. That was special! The locals and us foreigners together enjoyed those evenings.

* * *

Before we left Thailand, we flew to Bangkok for a day tour to see the Grand Palace, the Reclining Buddha, and the Emerald Buddha. Talk about grandiose!

Our group of massage therapists were ready to fly home. We spent the day in Bangkok and then headed to the airport to fly back east. There were a few in our group who decided to go home earlier or stay longer to visit other parts of the country.

I was ready to get back home. My coworkers and clients were anxiously awaiting back home.

We left Bangkok and headed to Seoul, South Korea, during a thunder and lightning storm at night. Then from Seoul, we left at 11:30 a.m. on that Sunday. Our pilots caught a tailwind that helped us fly back in time, crossing the International Date Line, arriving in Atlanta 11:10 a.m. that same Sunday. Twenty minutes before we left. That makes your head spin!

Home Again

I was gone for three weeks and everyone was excited to hear about the trip. The chiropractors and staff, the ladies at the salon, and other clients wanted to know about Thailand and were all anxious for me to demonstrate some of the new things I had learned.

People I know just didn't go to vacation in Thailand. But we saw people from all over the world. People who have the time and money, or no money, travel to these places to explore the world. We also saw many people who were backpackers traveling through the city as well as people in elaborate air-conditioned coaches.

But it was good to be home!

When I explained how most of the massages were done on the floor, and we had learned to transition to a table, most people frowned, not liking the thought of lying on the floor to get massaged. There were some clients who couldn't get up if they had to get down on the floor. Some were willing to try, but I needed time to practice, and being on the floor was difficult for me and my knees. It was not something I could do readily.

There are many people here in the States who do authentic Thai massage, and those that have taken advance classes to do the elaborate poses and stretches with a client. But one must be flexible, or you will become flexible—or dare I say, possibly hurt.

We renamed it "Tabletop Thai"! That way I could incorporate some of the therapies I had learned.

It was an experience of my lifetime for which I'm glad I had the opportunity. The experience as a whole broadened my senses as I learned a lot of history and the true meaning of massage.

I use some of the techniques in almost every massage I do, especially the trigger-point therapy. My massages are uniquely catered to each client. I choose what I think at the time is best for my client that I am working on. That's why I call it "Lynn's Massage and Bodywork"!

I didn't add Thai massage to my business card, but I do have bragging rights to say I studied Thai massage in Thailand!

Chapter 28
Kids Need Massages Too!

There was a mom who had a child needing massages due to a birth defect. I felt honored to help a mom of a four-year-old son with a condition that caused his hand and fingers to be drawn up. I forget now what it was labeled, but she brought him for me to massage. The first time he came, he was a bit apprehensive of having me massage him, of course. His mom sat in a chair in the corner of the room watching as I massaged his small neck and shoulders. I could feel the implanted wires under the skin on both sides of his neck. When I asked about them, she said they were for stimulation from an implant in his brain for the arm and hand to help his movement. She was taught a few massage strokes to help him as he grew. She brought him in to see if I could help in any way, and I was glad to show her a few of my techniques. Weeks later he started asking to see me, but only when mom was tired or maybe could learn something new. The last time I saw him he was 6. He was growing up and improving with hope that he would grow out of some of it.

A Girl Gymnast, Age Twelve

The chiropractor, Dr. K., came out of his office to ask if I could look at a gymnast.

"Sure. What's the problem?"

"She has a groin pull, and I adjusted her, but I thought you would be better at what she needs."

"Uh . . . How old is she?"

"Twelve." Both of us looked at each other with that look that said, *Uh, I don't want to do it, you do it.*

"She will be more comfortable with you than me," he said.

"Is her mom here?" I asked. And as I started to ask what she was wearing, the little girl came out of the room she was in, and Dr. K. introduced her to me.

"This is Lynn, our massage therapist, and she is going to try to help you," he said.

I looked down at her small size. She had tanned skin and dark hair.

Way too small for twelve, I thought. But my saving grace was that she was wearing spandex leggings.

Whenever I work on kids, I always ask them to wear spandex. Boys or girls. I can work through that fabric without them getting undressed or made to feel uncomfortable. I also ask that girls wear sports bras, since it helps them feel secure.

I brought a chair into the room for her mom who also had an infant carrier with the little sister in it. Then I began asking her some pertinent questions about what she was doing when she felt it hurt.

"Okay," I said. "I see quite a few gymnasts and try to help them the best I can. I have two sons who were football players, and I have three grandkids. My granddaughter is your age, and she is a cheerleader. I'd rather her be a gymnast like you." And I saw her smile at that. Right away, I tried to connect with her and put her at ease by sharing that I understood and she was not alone in that and it happened to others.

"Why?" she asked. Good, now I had her engaged and asking me a question.

"It's my preference of gymnastics over cheerleading. My granddaughter is a flyer and I fear someone will miss catching her, and I've seen more injuries in cheerleading than gymnastics. That's my opinion. Let's look at you."

Now I had her confidence and she smiled through her discomfort and got on the table as I directed her.

Her mom was watching and asking questions. Then I let the girl know, "I will tell you everything I do before I do it and if anything—anything at all—makes you uncomfortable, let me know and I will stop. Understand?" She nodded; her face was sad and I could tell she was in pain.

She relaxed for me as I talked her through each stretch and pressure point. I showed her a few stretches as we practiced that she could do on her own. She felt the release as I did, and she smiled a little. I asked if she was a good big sister and she said "yes." She was limber as rubber, responded well, and was good to go in thirty minutes.

She and her mom and baby sister were on their way. I inquired a few days later and the receptionist said they had called the next day and her mom said she was feeling great. "Music to my ears!"

I have to earn the trust of a client no matter the age or gender. Knowing a little about the sport helps too, to talk their language.

Chapter 29
Retired from All

Working from Home

After working at the chiropractors' office for ten years, I said enough. Time to move aside and give the opportunity to someone else. My husband wanted me to be home, I had a few clients and neighbors who saw me exclusively there, and I would build up my home-base office and just work from home.

But I didn't just do mild-mannered massage. Most of my clients needed special work, and I needed to keep myself strong and not wear myself out in order to keep working. I cut back to only four clients a day, and sometimes, on rare occasions, five or six. I cannot do that every day.

Special Circumstances

One of my regulars had to move his appointment from a Tuesday to a Thursday because his wife was very ill and undergoing chemo treatments for lung cancer. I tried to keep Thursdays open for me time, but he had no other time to come but 8:30 a.m. on Thursday, so I agreed to see him. He would be my only client for that day unless something else came up.

Which it did.

The next day, I had a voicemail from a friend I hadn't seen in over a year, asking if I still did massages and would like to schedule an appointment. I sent a text saying she could come in Thursday afternoon. *I would need extra time for her*, I thought to myself. It had been about a year since her husband died of lung cancer.

I knew I would need time after seeing both of them. Time needed for me to recoup from them.

The gentleman was highly stressed watching his wife of fifty-seven years go through what he called, in his words, "the barbaric process of radiation and chemotherapy" for her lung cancer. He had been through two bypass surgeries and other health issues during his life, and she had been the picture of health all those years. She was his rock!

"Who would have ever thought she could go before me," he said through tears. "I don't know what I would do without her." I massaged him to give him comfort and listened. He also admitted they had a large group of church groups and other prayer groups for support, and that meant so much to them. He had to hang in there, but he needed the massage if for nothing else than for me to listen with my hands-on gift of touch.

He came back a week later feeling better and said she was showing signs of improvement too.

Later that day, my other client arrived for her massage. She came in and I gave her a big, welcoming hug, which she needed. I still couldn't believe her husband was gone. He had passed away exactly one year the day she left me that voicemail. I was glad she came in, and no one else would be there so we could take our time.

"Who would have ever thought he would go before

me!" she said, the same words like a record repeating, the same day. The sadness they both had drew energy out of the room and me, but it was necessary to listen. "I'm the one who had breast cancer and survived the chemo. Twice! He died two days before our forty-fourth wedding anniversary! I needed this massage. Tomorrow I'm going out to celebrate our forty-fifth anniversary . . . without him. Don't know where yet!" She raised her empty hand as if a toast to them.

"As you should," I told her. " Ernie and I are so blessed, and we say it every day. Next year will be fifty years for us." We hugged a long hug again before she left. The massage made her a little lethargic, and she was going home to her pets to rest and to celebrate what they had.

I, too—after working on these two, highly stressed people—needed a nap to restore myself.

Alzheimer's and Other Illnesses

Joan, an elder lady with onset dementia, who was brought in by her daughter-in-law, loved massages and foot reflexology. She told me her feet were numb and having them rubbed and massaged gave her the joy of feeling her feet again. Although, it made her have itchy feet afterward. It drove her crazy, but she got to feel her feet. As we talked, she repeated herself several times, but we all did that sometimes.

Massage is good for those who are sedentary, and Joan, for instance, got a body and foot massage, and she loved it. Plus, I got to learn a lot from her, as she rambled about her life.

The elderly have more atrophy as they age if they don't move. Everyone will atrophy if we don't move, no matter what age.

The more sedentary we are, the more stiff we become.

I have a few patients with psoriatic arthritis, and the specific joints it attacks in the body are often referred for massage. If they have that, they also have psoriasis.

Ankylosing Spondylitis patients are also recommended to seek out massage.

Sciatica is a big one. At some time or another, I suspect everyone can have a sciatic nerve talk to them, and massage and stretching is usually recommended.

I had an appointment with my cardiologist and as the wait became rather lengthy, I picked up a pamphlet in the office and read it. It was guidelines and usual dos and don'ts about the heart, strokes, circulation, stress, and a few other morsels of information, which I found informative.

When I was called back, finally, to see the doctor, I carried it with me. When he came in, I showed him the pamphlet, and said I had read it numerous times front to back and didn't see one word about massage therapy and how it relieves stress and helps improve circulation.

He laughed at me out loud and told me I could get a massage if I wanted to, it wouldn't hurt me.

"No, sir, you don't understand," I said. "I AM a massage therapist. Have been for twenty years. And I don't need the work. I just think it should be mentioned here in a pamphlet like this, to inform people massage is good for stress relief and improving circulation. That's all."

Hidden Asset?

A businessman once called me this. When I asked about it, he told me his work was extremely stressful and his regular massages helped. I've also been told I was written off as an expense. Hmm. What is really flattering is when I hear, "My wife/husband told me to come see you."

Suppose I could add "Hidden Asset" to my business card?

Being Neighborly

Our neighbor, who lives less than half a mile away, has been a regular once-a-month client at my house for a few years. She is a nurse and works in another spa that does medical spa procedures.

She called me one morning just as I was going out the door to the office. To my shock, she told me she had just been moved out of the ICU to a regular room in the hospital.

"I got sepsis, and I am now out of the ICU after three days and am very swollen from the meds I've been given. If you have the time, can you please come to the hospital to help with the swelling in my legs? I've never been this big; I have forty pounds of fluid in my body."

I couldn't believe what I was hearing. She was close to dying from sepsis.

> *My mother had Alzheimer's, but her death certificate said she died of sepsis. She couldn't tell anyone how sick she was.*

How could I say no? I rechecked my schedule and didn't need to be at the chiropractors' office for a couple of hours. So, I grabbed my purse and a jar of massage cream and headed for the door. I opened the garage door and started to get into the car, but thought to double-check the side door of the garage to make sure it was locked.

As I rushed toward the side door, I had to go around the other vehicle in the garage and tripped as I rounded the front of it. I hit my shoulder and head on the side of the car and then landed hard on the concrete floor. I had bumped my head on the concrete, knocking my glasses off, and my knee was hurt.

I laid there assessing my damage. Thoughts flooded my brain. My head hurt and my knee was in agony. I thought I broke my knee. That was not good. I was afraid to get up by myself. I could pass out.

My phone, where was my phone? It was in my pants pocket. Hoping it wasn't broken, I rolled slightly from my side to my back, looking up from the floor of the garage. My patella was broken, I just knew it. If I got up without help, I could pass out.

Head trauma, I thought. My phone—thank God I had my phone.

Ernie had left a little earlier that morning for a dental appointment, so he was unavailable. But we did have a construction worker at the back of the house doing some repairs for us. I couldn't think of any neighbors close in our subdivision I could call. I was able to call the construction worker and asked him to come to the garage to assist me, please.

He came into the open garage door, calling for me, and I called back that I was on the floor next to the other car.

"I'm sorry," I told him. "I'm afraid to get up without assistance because I think my knee may be broken. I hit my head and feel dazed."

He helped me up and onto a chair that was sitting against the wall.

"Whew," I said. "I'm not dizzy."

"Lynn, should I call 911 or Ernie?" he asked.

"No! I think I'm okay. My knee is not broken but it hurts. I'm not dizzy. Please help me up, and if I can take a couple of steps and get into my office, I'll be okay."

I hobbled into my office with his help and thanked him

for his assistance, and he left back to his work. I raised my pant leg and applied arnica oil and massaged it into my poor bruised knee. I had to ease that pain.

"Thank you, Lord!" I kept repeating. "That's what I get for being in a rush." Arnica oil, tablets, and an ice pack—they would be my friends for the next week. They took the edge off for now. But I wanted to get to the hospital to help my neighbor friend. I told her I was coming to see her. I couldn't not go.

I got two ice packs out of the freezer so I could have a spare and folded it around my knee as I drove to the hospital.

Sally looked awful as she sat up in her hospital bed, with her legs uncovered, as she was overheated from swelling. Both her legs looked like elephant legs. We talked a few minutes, and I began working on her feet and ankles just to press the fluid from her swollen legs.

She had a catheter, and as I massaged her legs, I kept an eye on the bag for changes in color.

There was a noticeable reduction in her legs in the hour I was there, but there was still a long way to go. I was getting tired after my own injury, but I didn't mention that.

She offered to pay me, but I refused any payment for this, as it was a good-neighbor house call. My gift to her after the ordeal she had gone through. I was glad to have her as a neighbor and a regular client.

I needed to get back to the office after that. I drove the entire way with an ice pack on my knee. What a day!

Chapter 30
Frequently Asked Questions

People ask me if my hands hurt, and the answer is sometimes but it's usually first thing in the morning when I wake up. Early in my practice, my hands would swell from overwork, and I would plunge them in ice water. Those beginning years, my hands and arms took a lot of abuse from overwork. Too much, too soon.

As I have conditioned over the years, I built up a tolerance and endurance strength in both arms and hands. I don't have that problem as much. Washing dishes in the evening with hot water is like a hot bath after a long day. It feels good to my hands and they're less apt to be swollen the next morning.

Protect my hands. I had a paper cut on my finger once and since it was superficial and didn't bleed, I brushed it off. The next day, I had four one-hour massages, and by the end of the day, I noticed my finger was getting sore where that paper cut was.

The end of my index finger had gotten infected from a minor paper cut! I pinched it a little, and it then bled and was infected. It took two weeks for that to heal.

I no longer take minor scratches or cuts for granted with my hands. When I cut myself in the kitchen, it is a serious matter. I cannot massage with a cut on my hands. My husband is always cautioning me to wear my gloves out in the garden. I must wear finger cots or surgical gloves when I have a wound on my hands.

Pain and hormone patches are something people have stuck on them that I need to be aware of too! I ask clients if they are taking any medications I need to be aware of. Especially blood thinners so as not to bruise.

Do I See Auras?

Yes, sometimes. I saw the aura of a person first by accident. It took me by surprise the first time, but it was incredible. What a gift, I thought, to be able to see that. I look for it sometimes when I get a good connection with a person, but it doesn't always come through. It takes practice. I have some people who are actually what I call "white lighters." They exude a white light. They walk into a room and the room brightens. I've also seen the opposite.

Do You Know Chakras or Feel Them?

Yes and yes, I sometimes feel them. Mostly the heart chakra. I actually had an episode once where a heart chakra of a man threw my hand off him through his back. It was startling, and I didn't know what it was or how. But it was during a class, and this guy was facedown, so I asked a colleague to come over and feel the energy this guy was giving off, and we sort of played with it. We could feel the energy in a cylindrical form about two feet above his middle back. We waved our hands through it and pushed it back and forth.

Lots of crown chakras can be felt. Usually when I'm sitting at the head doing traction. One client released something pent up and it hit me so hard in the chest, it took my breath away. Her husband was sitting in a chair near me, and they both heard me gasp for air, but I didn't say anything. Then she said, "I don't know what you just did, but I feel lighter."

"Whatever you released just hit me in the chest, that's what made me gasp!" She apologized if I was hurt by it. It startled me but I was more amused.

I've gotten used to things happening that can't always be explained. I resigned to expect the unexpected and appreciate it too! Just like the electrical charge I get from some folks, especially after a surgery or injury. I feel for it and can tell which dermatome it is contained in.

I am always glad I can be instrumental in whatever needs to happen. I am blessed!

How Do You Always Seem to Know Where It Hurts?

That's what I do with the information your body gives me. I can pinpoint the area of the belly and the muscle where lactic acid is built up and work it out. Or lymph nodes. Those little areas of plumbing under our skin can get a clog, and when I rub over it, it can be a little "owie."

"What was that? Touch it again."

"It doesn't hurt now."

"Good thing you're getting a massage to work out your lymphatic system! That's detoxing!"

Massage improves blood circulation. It takes a minute for a drop of arterial blood to pump out of the heart to your big toe, filter through the arterioles to the veins, and return to the heart via the lung. IMPROVE circulation, NOT increase.

Massage is wringing out the gunk from the tissues in your body, blood, and lymphatic systems!

That's my interpretation.

Doctor Script

Some people will come in with a written note from their doctor asking me if I know what this or that muscle is. Generally, their doctor or physical therapist refers them for a massage and will write down the muscle that needs to be addressed or massaged. Most often that muscle is the piriformis where the sciatic nerve is affected, which is in the hip along with the gluteus maximus. It's why hip flexors are important. Everything in and around the body is important too.

I ask new clients what they do on a daily routine, what kind of work or workout routine they do on a regular basis. Anyone sitting at a desk is neck and shoulders, and I target those areas most. If they are runners, I'll incorporate a little extra time on the feet and legs.

My Clients Are as Therapeutic For Me as I Am to Them!

We share sadness and joy together! I've been through births and birthdays with clients; the loss of a loved one, both them and I; engagements, weddings, and divorces; and illnesses. Long illnesses, either them or a spouse or loved one. And even pets! Pets are welcome in my massage area, and sometimes they want a little massage too. I am happy to oblige, and they love it!

I've met some massage therapists who have moved

their practice from humans to animals, like dogs or horses.

We build up a relationship over the months and years. Some clients are on a regular weekly or monthly basis, depending on their health, work, or workouts. Even mental conditions from an abusive relationship, accident, or some sort of chronic health issue.

We have self-defense mechanisms built into us. When we are hurt physically or mentally, a massage can help break down that negative defense mechanism and reintroduce positive muscle memory again.

I use a saying when someone comes to me long after an accident, when they still have their "self-preservation mechanisms" turned on. That's when they still don't want to move or be touched for fear it will hurt. I have an occasional client who will see me six months after an accident, still afraid to move their neck for fear it may hurt. After a few strokes on the levator muscle from the shoulder to the neck, it will relax and the pain will be gone. I'm a hero! Not really, but the body didn't know it could move that way after being traumatized. I just reintroduced positive muscle memory and the pain alleviated.

How Often Should I Get a Massage?

If everyone had a massage once a month, we would be healthier—that's my opinion! But time and money and stress levels will most likely dictate that.

I've heard I was on the expense account a time or two!

If we could stretch that from four to six weeks for a

body tune-up, I think there would be less illness in the world. Ideally every two weeks if time and money would allow.

I had a massage magazine article back in 2000, written about Bob Hope, that said he had a massage every day. Even on his USO tours, his therapist flew with him and would have his hands and feet massaged between shows. He even attributed his longevity to his massage therapist. He lived to be one hundred.

The Listening Touch!

It does wonders for a person with mental, physical, or emotional pain.

A hands-on . . . gift!

Acknowledgments

Thanks to my family.—my husband of fifty years and my two sons, Lee and Elton, my daughter-in-law, Diane, and my three grandchildren, Tobias, Caden, and Aleke!

They are my inspiration.

I woke up one morning, sat straight up in bed, and told myself I needed to write a book. About what? My experiences being a massage therapist! And, eventually, I want to co-write a true story with my son Elton about a baby bird he saved from dying that needs to be told.

But first, let me learn by telling my own story. Every day, I tell myself and my clients that I should write a book about some of the experiences I've encountered in my twenty years as a massage therapist.

People like hearing stories as I work on soothing away their stress, body aches, and pains. And sometimes, it is just what they need to take their thoughts away from their own stress and relax the mind as well as the body. It can also create thoughts of their own to share a memory.

True experiences along my journey in life.

I feel so blessed to have my health so I can give comfort or a healing touch to those in need of it.

I listen with ears, heart, and touch.

Sensitivity vs. Sensibility

I hope you enjoy reading some of my experiences.

Thank you to J. C. for helping me with the title.

About the Author

Linda "Lynn" F. Dubois grew up in rural Ohio. She and her husband, Ernie, reside in North Georgia. She is a massage therapist who attended the Dayton School of Medical Massage. From there, the adventure of massage therapy has taken her on a journey through twenty-plus years! She shares some of her experiences as a massage therapist, learning different techniques like reflexology, active isolated stretching, and myoskeletal alignment. She spent two years learning cranial sacral therapy, Level I through IV, to develop her own Listening Touch. Her discovery of massage therapy has taken her halfway around the world to Thailand to experience Swe-Thai and Thai foot massage, going back to the roots of massage while wanting to keep up with the times to help people who come to see her for the myriad of health concerns they may have.

For relaxation, she likes to do vegetable and flower gardening to get her hands and feet in the dirt to detox and keep grounded.

It has been a memorable journey that she wanted to share with readers.